In My Father's House

In My
FATHER'S
HOUSE

Grace Nies Fletcher

McGraw-Hill Book Company, Inc.

New York   Toronto   London

To Jock

For understanding a writer's many moods

Preface

WHEN my friends ask, "What is your new book about?" I always hesitate. If I say, "About my father," will they not think this merely a biography of a strangely happy man who saw through sickness, poverty, and even death to the glory beyond? Actually, this is the history of a vital period in our development as a nation, as seen through one man's eyes . . . the era of firm faith in God and in our future as a Christian democracy.

Lee Nies grew up in a clear-eyed young America that was not ashamed to put "In God We Trust" upon its silver coins, a tacit admission that where man ends, God begins. The Horatio-Alger state of mind, if you will, when nothing was impossible, but a period of great power because we believed in ourselves and in our God-guided destiny. Men and nations can grow only as high as their ideals. We knew then, quite simply, that if we strayed from these, we should go down to defeat as surely as had Rome and Babylon; and we cherished the childlike (but not childish) faith that freedom under God was eminently possible, not only for ourselves but for all men.

What a far cry is this certainty from our present-day jitteriness! Catapulted into world leadership, we are not just sure we want to lead or where to go. One demagogue shouts, "This way!" and another, "What's the use? We can't save the whole world."

No, we cannot, but the Son of God has; and only through Him can our own path be made clear. A positive, singing faith draws all men unto itself. It is small use to cry, "Down with the anti-Christ! Down with communism!" unless we also cry, "Up with God!" Unless we find again the certainty by which our fathers stood; unless we, like them, are willing to die—and live—for this belief, we shall never lead anyone anywhere except into our own confusion.

We need to hear again the clear trumpet call of faith in a living God and in His plan for us. Lee Nies had this faith. He was part of the great procession of those who march, singing, toward a sure goal; who are not afraid of anything in this world or the next; who know that freedom under God is not for any one man or nation. "In my Father's house are many mansions."

GRACE NIES FLETCHER

Contents

In My Father's House

CHAPTER I

The White Bean of Liberty

THIS IS THE STORY of a boy who had nothing—and everything. Who outgrew even the vast horizons of Texas where a man may stretch to his full stature, as well as the book learning of Massachusetts; so the Lord called to him, "Come up here, son, and help me fling out a few stars!"

Lee Nies, my dad, was a big man in every sense of the word. He stood six feet, weighed over two hundred, and had a rugged profile such as artists chisel upon mountains; but when he smiled, it was as if a sunset had blazed behind his craggy face, making it suddenly magnificent. He enjoyed just being alive so hugely that traveling salesmen were always asking him into the Pullman washroom for "a quick one" and being surprised when he refused. One of them asked him what line he was traveling for.

"Well, I started out rustling telegrams in a saloon in Texas," Dad admitted. "But right now I'm in the fishing business in Boston, partners with Peter and Andrew—and Jesus Christ." When the man looked scared at having offered a minister a drink, Dad added, "You know something? I found the same kind of customers in both places, the saloon and the church, partly good and partly bad—like me."

Like his great Partner, Dad knew how mean people could be

but still loved them. He used to tell a story about a scientist who crossed a spider with a butterfly and achieved a monster, part of which fought to crouch in dark corners, waiting to pounce upon its victims, while the other half yearned to flutter its bright wings in the wide sky. People are like that, Dad said, tearing themselves apart until they decide which shall be triumphant, the spider or the butterfly. The minister's magnificent job was to point the way back into the sunshine of God's presence to those who fell into dark corners. As Chris Crane did.

Chris was head usher at the biggest Methodist church in New England where Lee used to preach to thousands of worshipers who crowded the pews every Sunday. Chris was a stocky, striking-looking man whose dark, quirked eyebrows contrasted with his shock of silver hair and in whose immaculate coat lapel a fresh white carnation always flared. He held himself so proudly erect as he marched down the aisle with the collection plate that Lee used to chuckle to himself, "All Chris needs is a trumpet to make a parade!"

Chris gave a great deal of his time to the church and to charity; when the hospital needed a new wing or the Community Fund was lagging, someone always said, "Phone Chris!" He was a born sales-man who gloried in doing things in a large way. "Think big, act big, and the money will take care of itself," he insisted. "Why waste time on little details?" When it was proposed to retire the mortgage on his own church, Chris cried, "Let's add up the mort-gages on all the Methodist churches in town; clean 'em *all* up, while we're about it!" When the money came pouring in, church bells rang and people laughed and cried, marveling, "Chris has done it again!"

It didn't seem possible that this could be the same man who came bursting into Lee's parsonage study one day, almost incoherent with fear. "Lee, you've got to help me!" Chris cried, trembling all over. "I must have twenty thousand dollars right off or I'm going to jail!"

This amount was four times Lee's own yearly salary, but he merely pushed a chair toward the frightened man, urging, "Tell me what's wrong, Chris."

When Chris told him what had happened, Lee decided to call a meeting of the entire official board of his church that night at the parsonage; though what, if anything, they could or would do to save Chris was a question he could not answer. "Be here at eight," Lee told him. But Chris was there walking up and down, up and down the front parlor an hour before the rest arrived. Finally the chairman of the board said crisply, "We're all here. For heaven's sake, Chris, sit down!"

But he couldn't. Chris stood there, clutching the shabby parlor table so hard his big knuckles were white as he explained that many of the policyholders of the life insurance company for which he worked sent him their checks which he deposited in his personal account, deducting his commission, and later giving the company account a single check for what was due. This was common practice. But the new house Chris was building had cost more than he'd figured, so he'd delayed putting the insurance money into the bank—so the inspector had arrived this morning to find the company account short. "Someone who wants my job must have tipped him off to come just now," Chris cried. "He isn't due for another month!"

"How much do you still need?" one board member asked.

When Chris told him, the rest gasped. Chris added hastily that he'd sold all his stocks and bonds, the new house, even his car at a loss, but the time was so short. . . . "If I don't get that money in the bank by tomorrow morning, I'll be liable for arrest!" Great beads of perspiration were running down his wet forehead. "Even if I don't go to jail, I'll never get another agency. I'll be ruined for life!"

"Just one of those 'little details'?" a rival insurance man who'd always been jealous of Chris's success asked acidly. "I suppose you planned to pay it all back? That's what they always tell the judge."

Chris turned very white. If his own friends in the church didn't believe him. . . . Shock, embarrassment, unbelief were written large upon the circle of accusing faces turned to his. Chris Crane, head usher, builder of churches and hospitals, a common thief! As he stared at them, Chris's thick body seemed to shrink inside his natty clothes till they were too big for him and the Gethsemane

agony in his eyes was more than Lee could bear. It's a bitter thing
to watch a condemned man lose all hope. Lee got to his feet and
faced his official board sternly.

"Gentlemen," Lee demanded, "is there a man here who's never
shaded a business deal in his life? Not in actual words, maybe, but
in something he didn't say?"

No one answered him directly, but the front parlor was suddenly so still Lee could hear the glass clock the Ladies' Aid had
given him ticking up on the mantel and Chris's heavy breathing
as he waited for their verdict. After an eternity the chairman said
slowly, "I could lend you a couple of thousand, Chris, if that
would help." "I'll put a second mortgage on my house for another
three," another man offered, and others chimed in. By the time
they'd finished, Chris had no more to fear from tomorrow's dawn.

Lee was so proud of them all as he stood there, his face radiant
and his hand on Chris's shoulder, for this night not only one man
had been born again to a new chance, but each of his church leaders
had grown up from his childhood in Christian living to the vast,
forgiving tolerance of an adult son of God.

Lee did not achieve overnight his knowledge that failure and
success were the alternate steps by which we mount toward God;
his tolerance was partly the result of earning his own way in a
difficult world since he was nine, and partly a heritage from his
own father's fierce love of freedom. Grandpa Nies had died long
before my brother Ike and I were born, but we knew him intimately from hearing Dad's tales about his fiery father. No matter
how big an audience Dad was to address that evening or where
he and Mother were going to dinner, to the mayor's or to the
governor's, Dad never missed telling us children our "goodnight
story" after our early supper. Ike was so handsome he should have
been the girl. When I was six he was three, with enormous violet
eyes, thick golden hair in a "Dutch clip," and an enchanting grin
that made the Ladies' Aiders slip him candy in church; while my
fine straight hair flew every which way and the silver-rimmed
spectacles I had to wear kept slipping down my inadequate nose.

"Don't worry, Susie; real beauty comes from the inside out,"
Dad soothed one evening as the three of us sat snugly together in

his big study armchair. "You'll be better-looking when you're sixty than when you're six." It was small comfort to have to wait till you were old to be beautiful. I pinched Ike till he howled and Dad warned, "Remember the spider, you two! What shall I tell you tonight?"

"Grampa Nies and the White Bean of Liberty!" we yelled together. It was our favorite story, a family heirloom of which we knew every word, every comma even, and corrected Dad sternly when he even stopped for breath in the wrong place. Ike cried, twisting the front lock of his hair as he did when excited, "The sodgers came marching, marching! 'N Grampa said—"

" 'Pack up the feather bed, Bowitt!' " I burst in, unwilling to be left out. " 'We're going to America!' "

"Hey, who's telling this story?" Dad demanded, and we kids knew it was time to pipe down if we didn't want to be sent to bed without hearing Dad tell how he found out what it meant to be an American.

Your grandpa, George Nies, met your grandma, Bowitt, on a dance floor in Neu-Isenburg, Germany, a little town near the Black Forest. George's family had been Huguenots—that means Protestants who'd fled from France to escape the bloody religious massacres—so he went to the Lutheran church; while Bowitt's mother was a Roman Catholic. Bowitt (as her friends called her, though her real name was Barbara) was a little slip of a girl with black hair and snapping brown eyes, not much taller than a whip but strong from working in the fields, raising vegetables. She hoed barefooted to save her shoes for Sunday, digging her toes into the warm brown earth. (Always be glad, Dad told Ike and me, that you had a grandmother rooted in the good earth from which comes the strength to hold on when the going gets rough, as it does for everyone, sooner or later.) She had a quick mind too, and was such a beggar for reading that the Lutheran minister to whom she delivered vegetables loaned her Goethe and the classics. But more than anything, Bowitt loved music.

So did your Grandpa George; its rhythm was as natural to him as his own heartbeat. He was at a dance at the Town Hall one

evening when he looked up and saw Bowitt standing there alone
in the doorway. Her body, whip-slim and lovely, was swaying
unconsciously to the music, and when she lifted her eyes to his
there was fire and laughter in them. George knew who she was,
of course, but he'd never spoken to her. He didn't now; he just
went to her with his arms out and she danced into them. They
were engaged when he took her home that first night.

Naturally the whole village buzzed with excitement when the
Lutheran minister married them, but George and Bowitt did not
care, for they were fiercely in love. George was a shoemaker; not
a cobbler, you understand, but an artist who created each shoe
from the hide to the last smooth lacing for the foot it was to grace.
He owned his own house with the shop in front, and before long
he and Bowitt had four children, two boys and two girls, to dance
around the Tannenbaum, the Christmas tree with its shining candle
eyes. They were very happy until that fateful day when the Prussians marched into Neu-Isenburg to draft every able-bodied young
man for Bismarck's growing army.

George hated Bismarck. "That Prussian bully!" he'd storm to
Bowitt. "First he gobbled up little Denmark; now he's needling the
big bear, Austria. Then it will be France's turn."

"Sh!" Bowitt warned in a panic. "Someone will hear you!"

George glanced at his small wife speculatively. "I have had a
letter from our cousins in America. Now there is a country for you
where one man is as good as another. . . ."

Bowitt sprang to her feet, catching her breath in almost a sob.
"My home is here. I will not go to America, do you hear? You
cannot make me!"

George shouted back, "Neither will that dumbhead ever get me
into his army!"

But of course he did. The day the Prussians marched into Neu-
Isenburg, tramp, tramp, tramp, the thunder of their boots upon
the cobblestones struck terror into every home. A notice tacked
up on the Town Hall warned that every man of military age who
did not register would be regarded as a deserter and shot. George
had to go. He was assigned to the cavalry. He came home with
black despair in his heart to tell Bowitt he had to leave the next day.

"No time to find an apprentice to run my shop," George bewailed bitterly as his little family clustered, frightened, about him. "How can you with four small children go out to work again in the fields? You will starve. What is to become of my son Henry? My George? My Anna here? My baby, Mary Elizabeth, with her big brown eyes like her mother's?"

The children all began to cry and Bowitt tried to hush them, but tears were running down her own cheeks. So George had to draw himself together. "Now, now, this will not do," he chided, picking up the baby and wiping her nose. "Let us all get down upon our knees and pray the good Lord to show us a way out of this trouble."

But this he said merely to comfort them, for he knew it was no use. The Lord had no commission in the Prussian Army.

George Nies reported for duty the next morning, along with the rest of his neighbors, to a Prussian officer who had a great red scar from a dueling sword drawing down one corner of his mouth, so that he seemed forever grinning at some macabre joke.

"Line up and count off by tens!" he roared.

All the women and children of the village had followed their men to the village square, yearning for a last sight of their husbands, sons, or brothers, but the Prussians pushed them back so roughly a child screamed. To these haughty officers the peasants were merely so much dirt under their booted feet. George, seeking for Bowitt with his eyes, did not notice that a soldier had stopped in front of him, and was offering him something in a steel helmet.

"Take one, you clodhopper!" the soldier snarled, shaking the helmet. "Did you never see a bean before, fool?"

George reached out a shaking hand, took a bean, and clenched it in his fist without looking at it, for hot anger had surged through him. He was as good a man as this sneering Prussian! Yet he dared not cry out that this was so, or hit back at the oaf who had called him a fool; instead George merely stood there like a dumb, goaded ox. Humiliation rose, a sickness in his throat that he should so act the coward before his own sons!

"Those who hold the white bean, one step forward, march!" the Prussian officer barked. George opened his clenched fist, and his bean was white. What did it mean? He took a step forward, waited, trembling. "It is a fair lottery," the officer explained. "There are nine black beans and one white one for each squad. The man who has drawn the white bean is excused from military duty for one year. The rest of you—forward, march!"

The white bean—I have the white bean of liberty; I do not have to fight! The words trumpeted inside George's head as he stood there, too dazed with relief to move till Bowitt ran to him, tears of joy running down her cheeks, gasping, "The Lord answered our prayer! It is a miracle! We have another year together."

And what was that? A rope about the neck that had not been jerked. Exultation ran out of George. But there was a country where a man need never be a dumb ox, where he could hold up his head with anyone. . . . "Go home and pack the feather bed!" George roared to his wife Bowitt. "*We are going to America!*"

George was almost in a frenzy to get away, for the humiliation of that morning had gone deep. The white bean, he felt, was not only a reprieve; it was a sign to him that he must not bring up his sons to goose-step through the blood of Europe. Even if it cost him every penny he had to get to this America, it was well spent if his sons could look every man in the eye and not tremble, as their father had, before the might of the Prussian sabers. George sold his business, his snug little home, and took the first passage he could get on a sailing vessel rather than wait for one of the new steamships. It took six weeks to reach New York, and Bowitt and the children were seasick all the way.

Even after they arrived in this country, George itched to get as far away from Germany as possible, but Bowitt was in no condition to travel farther. They went to relatives in Charles City, Iowa, where George's third son was born. He had white hair and too much nose and they named him for the friend who helped them get away.

"Leopold Adolf Nies!" Ike and I chanted together. "The baby was *you!*"

Dad nodded. He looked so big that it was hard to realize he'd ever been tiny, with hair like white cotton. He was six and had a new sister, Carrie, before his father finally got his little family as far away from Germany as he could go, to Dallas, Texas. They took a side-wheeler, the *Golden Eagle*, down the Mississippi to New Orleans, and then, still not satisfied, rode the railroad as far as it went. Lee never forgot what his father said when, tired and dirty from sitting up day and night, the children stumbled off the train at the end of the line in Dallas.

"Ve're here! And I'll lick any von of you who speaks again Cherman!" his father thundered. He took a deep breath of the clear, free Texas air where a man could bring up his sons as he chose. "From now on ve're Americans!"

So Dallas and Lee Nies grew out of knee pants together. It's hard to realize how young our country really is, Dad used to marvel. Why, the lifetime of one man could span the change from a town with unpainted wooden houses, gambling dens, and saloons on its main street to a proud, paved city with skyscrapers, art museums, and its own symphony orchestra!

Even when Lee was eight there was still a hog wallow in the middle of the main street. He and the rest of his gang of small boys used to ride the pigs like ponies down under the high wooden sidewalks that were raised up in front of the stores so the customers could stay out of the mud. Dallas was exciting on Saturday nights when the cowboys rode in off the cattle ranges, many of them for the first time in lonely months. They galloped into town, shooting out the street lights from sheer exuberance, with their pockets full of six months' pay and all the town wide open and red-hot to help them spend it. Cattle were more valuable than people, and the schools were always let out so that the pupils could go to the cattle-thief hangings. Young Lee used to think his father bitterly cruel because he would not let his eight-year-old take part in these festivities, complete with hot-tamale wagons and Mexican pecan candy.

"Much better you should vork," George Nies said firmly, for in spite of his determination to speak American he could not quite manage the letter "w" even yet.

But he was a respected businessman in town, busy enough to really need Lee's help. His shop was in the front of the new house he was buying for his family, for five children needed plenty of space; there would have been six if Henry, the eldest son, hadn't married and stayed in Iowa. Young Lee would fetch his father the tools and the leather from which he fashioned the wonderfully soft yet durable boots with high red heels, for which the cowboys were glad to pay a month's wages. For these were honest boots, capable of carrying a man safely through wind, rain, and the scorching Texas days. Law enforcement was still a more or less personal affair, when a man's very life might depend upon the strength of his shoe in the saddle or the speed of his draw with his gun. All of this George Nies tried to explain to his small, towheaded son, sulking because he could not see the hanging.

"Throw it away, Lee!" George Nies would roar when his son carelessly passed him a flawed piece of leather. "Should we build lies into a Nies shoe? Do you want to be responsible if a man is alone on the range with a thousand head of longhorns and our shoes give way? 'Honesty is the best policy'—bah. It is the very sole of the shoe itself. Give me another piece of good leather!"

Thus the father built himself into every shoe and built also into the mind of a little boy how big a thing it is to be born in a great country where a man can speak his own mind, work as he wills; to live in a place like Texas where he can grow outsize because the prairies have no end either, but flow on and on to far horizons where blood-red sunsets lap them, wave on wave, in the glory of God.

"Do you know why this country is great?" George asked young Lee one day as they worked together in the coolness of the shop while outside the hot Texas sun burned the deep dust of the road. But today Lee didn't mind staying, because his father was making him a pair of red-topped cowboy boots for his ninth birthday, which was only a week away. They were beautiful shoes, exactly like a cowboy's, only smaller; no other boy on the street would have a pair like them!

"Here." His father tossed Lee a silver quarter, ordering, "Read what it says, out loud." For there was pride in him that his son who was not yet nine could read English so fluently.

"Liberty. In God we trust." Young Lee read both sides of the coin, holding it tightly, for in those days a quarter was a great deal of money.

"You understand what that means?" George Nies thundered. "To be free to choose and to choose God's way is all that makes us different from the animals! Otherwise a man is no different from those Prussians' pigs, and he'd better go grunt and root. Keep the silver piece to remind you."

True, some things in Texas were not perfect, George admitted. The hangings, for instance, and the shootings. Far better if these wrongs could be righted in court, peaceably. But some mistakes were the price you paid for taming a raw, new country. Texas would grow up, just as Lee would grow. But the young country would grow up strong only as long as it believed—really believed—the trust it had minted upon its coins. George Nies drew a deep breath and beamed proudly at his son who was American-born, a citizen by birth.

"You, Lee! Listen to me!" George waved his hammer excitedly. "Perhaps someday you will walk into the White House and a man in striped pants will say to you, 'Good morning, Mr. President.' Hold up your head and say this to yourself: 'The white bean of liberty was given by God to my father, and so to me!' "

It came as a dreadful shock to Lee when his father was buried on the little boy's ninth birthday. It seemed like the end of everything. Less than a week ago his father had been sitting at his bench, making a pair of little red-topped cowboy shoes for Lee's birthday. And now the little red cowboy shoes, like no other boy on the street had, would never be finished. Maybe it was a selfish thing to think, but Lee knew that the boots and his father's love for him had been part and parcel of the same thing.

Their house was full of strange people, queer smells, and the sound of his mother Bowitt's voice, crying, "It is all so useless, so senseless a sacrifice. Ah, George, George, how could you leave me alone, alone in a strange land like a burning furnace?" For it was August 1 the day Lee's father was buried, and so hot that Lee could not bear to lie on his bed, but lay instead upon the cool matting on the floor. After breakfast, Lee sneaked off down to the river to fish for crawfish, for he wanted to get away from the still, cold body lying in the coffin in the darkened parlor. Surely that was not his passionate, warmhearted, trumpet-voiced father! But there was no water in the river; it had all dried up like the happiness inside Lee when the scared feeling came in. He had to go back home to be hustled into his shoes and suit to go to his father's funeral.

Bowitt was so harried it was small wonder that she forgot that the day her husband, George, the laughing boy into whose arms she had danced, was buried was also important to her small son, Lee. But she missed the boy when he did not come in to supper, and she found him sprawled out on the back porch, sobbing, his towhead buried in his skinny arms. Bowitt knelt beside him and put her hand gently upon his shoulder, telling him his father would not want him to grieve so, that he must now be her man.

"But I'm not crying only for Father," young Lee sobbed. "I'm nine years old today and nobody gave me a present!"

Bowitt laughed and she cried and she cradled her young son in her arms; and she thought that here she still had a part of her headstrong, wonderful George. She gave Lee a silver coin from her slim purse and told him to go to the store to buy his own present. Lee looked at the coin and was comforted: as he hurried along the road through the twilight to the store, it almost seemed as if his father had spoken to him, as if he couldn't be very far away; for the birthday gift clutched hard in his hand was a silver quarter, and on one side it said "Liberty" and on the other "In God we trust."

CHAPTER 2

The Making of a Man

THE FRIGHTENING GREEN LONELINESS of that great field of Texas corn where he got his first job hoeing, at two dollars a week—this was the thing young Lee remembered most vividly about that terrible first year after his father died. Texas corn often grows twelve feet high; Lee was only nine, small for his age and thin as a knife blade, and the heat of that Texas summer beat upon him like flails so that his body dripped sweat and frightened tears.

"That corn grew so high and so thick that I couldn't see any of the other workers," he used to explain. "I couldn't even see the sky!"

Hoeing there alone, the scared boy would hear queer rustles, noises that were maybe a rattler or some animal creeping upon him through the green gloom. At night he would wake in his bed, sobbing, dreaming that the tall green corn was falling on him, smothering him. But he always went back in the morning; and every Saturday night he laid two dollars in his mother's palm.

Bowitt took in washing in order to feed her growing family and to keep up the payments on the homestead which George had begun buying. Soon she had more work than she could handle, even with the boys to help her. Lee and George, Jr., had to draw endless buckets from the well out in the back yard as there was no running water in the house, but they did not mind, for they knew their mother worked harder than they did. Night after night they would fall asleep to the thump of her iron upon the ironing board, and often before they got up in the morning she would be at it again already, to take advantage of the coolness of dawn.

"We must keep the roof over our heads and this bit of ground," she warned them. "It is the only heritage your father left you." But washing brought little pay, not nearly enough to buy a house, so the children had to leave school. George, Jr., got a job as a Western Union messenger boy; the two girls, Anna and Mary Elizabeth, steamed out cotton flowers at a local milliner's; and Lee worked in his cornfield. There were many days when they ate only cornmeal mush and molasses, for Bowitt insisted upon setting aside the "house money" before they bought meat. The quarterly payment at the bank was an ever-hovering menace. Sometimes it seemed to young Lee, as he came home from hoeing too tired to speak and flung himself down upon the cool matting of the floor to rest, as if his father's high-flown words had been bitter nonsense.

"What freedom have we except to sweat and starve?" he asked himself. Many things he had taken for granted, like food and shelter, were not free at all. It was all right to say "In God we trust," but why didn't He do something about getting them a good steak once in a while? It had been weeks since the family had even tasted meat. Yet every Sunday their mother took them, washed, patched, and painfully clean, to sit in a neat row at the Methodist church; the penny clutched in each small hand was from his or her own earning, always laid aside carefully on payday. Lee, so weary he was half asleep, used to sit in the hard pew and wonder why the Lord didn't pass a miracle, like He did about the white bean, to let all of us go back to school. What good was it to live in a great, rich country, if none of this belonged to you?

Then something happened to show Lee that there were others who were not even as fortunate as he—and that like it or not, he had a wealth of which he had not known, simply because his skin was white.

Lee was delighted when his older brother, George, was able to get him a job too as messenger boy. Lee's uniform was furnished, but not his shoes, which he found anxiously, wore out in no time when you ran all over Dallas, especially in wet weather when you couldn't afford rubbers. His delivery route lay in the toughest but also the most exciting part of town, among the saloons and gambling "parlors" with their great gilt mirrors and shining bars where men just in from months on the range could forget their loneliness; where they pushed their wide-brimmed hats upon the back of their heads while they watched the roulette wheel spin; and where pay for six months of sweat and saddle sores was lost in a matter of seconds. Once Lee was kicked clear across the room by a gambler who thought the boy had broken his luck by interrupting to deliver a telegram! So Lee learned to wait till the wheel stopped spinning before handing over his yellow envelopes and to dodge before he was hit. Such lessons he learned when most boys were mastering fractions in school or learning to spell "Mississippi."

Lee was only nine when he saw a man murdered.

When the boy pushed open the swinging door to the saloon that afternoon and stood there looking over the men ranged along the bar, he could feel the tenseness in the air like a piece of elastic which has been stretched too far. He was just about to call "Telegram for Adam Short. Adam Short, please!" when a shot rang out, and someone screamed horribly. Lee's stomach went queasy with fear as he stared, wide-eyed, at the tall rancher leaning against the bar with a smoking six-shooter in his hand. The Mexican who had screamed staggered, fell to the floor, and his blood began running across in a tiny red stream toward where Lee was standing. The small boy was too terrified to move a muscle. The Mexican gave one final jerk and lay still, while Lee watched the horrible red stream come closer, closer, to his own shoe and he too paralyzed to move away.

"Wal, I reckon you put your brand on that Greaser, Shorty!" a man's voice drawled, breaking the almost unbearable tension. "He won't rustle no more o' yoah cattle."

The tall rancher laughed, put up his gun, and motioned the

bartender to "Set 'em for everyone. Only thing a Greaser under-stands is a bullet between the eyes," he said loudly. "Adam Short don't stand for no funny business."

Lee's hand jerked suddenly, as the Mexican had. *But Adam Short was the name on your yellow envelope! He'd just killed a man. You were supposed to go right up to a murderer.* . . . Bile rose in the little boy's throat as he pushed frantically at the swinging door.

"Hey, bud, who's that message for?" the bartender called, but Lee couldn't answer. He rushed outside just in time to vomit in the road.

On his way home that night, Lee tried to figure out what had happened. He wondered, Was it right to kill even a Greaser cattle thief without a trial? There were courts in Texas in those days but they were pretty lenient with a rancher protecting his herds, for not only his pocketbook but the breadbasket of the entire community was at stake. If the Greaser had been a white man, maybe they'd have sent for the sheriff. Yellow, black, and brown men might be legally free, but it surely didn't do for them to get biggety. For the first time Lee wondered if Negroes really liked living in shanties, being "Jim Crow." *You were lucky to be white.* Some people, it seemed, were freer than others in this great country.

Lee didn't dare tell his mother that he'd seen the shooting, or that he'd made a friend in a house of ill repute. Bowitt worried so. When she realized that Lee would have to go in and out of that particular district, she called him to her, explaining, "Those are bad women! Don't ever let one of them even touch you or you'll get a sickness."

"Like the fever Pa had?" the small boy asked, interested.

"Certainly not." His mother drew herself up, shocked. "We will talk no more about it. Isn't my word enough for you? If only we didn't have to have money. . . . Your uniform will protect you. Keep to yourself and you'll be all right."

Those girls might be a bad lot, as his mother had warned, but they tipped the best in town. With all his running about and un-balanced diet, Lee at ten was practically all blue eyes and a nose too big for his small, thin face, while his uniform hung upon his skinny shoulders as on a hanger. One cold, windy wet night Lee was glad when he saw by his address book that he had to go to that district again, for he was sure to be asked inside where it was bright and warm.

He was standing there in the front hall with its lovely red wallpaper and thick dry rug, waiting for his book to be signed and wishing he didn't have to go out again into the rain but could stay here, when a girl came running down the carpeted stairs so fast she almost knocked Lee down.

"Oh, I'm sorry!" she apologized and smiled at him. She had on a short, frilly gold dress and she looked mighty pretty, not sick at all. But, remembering what his mother had said, Lee drew back his arm. She cried, "What's the matter? I don't bite. Why, you're only a kid!"

Lee's completely charming smile changed him from a hipless youngster whose uniform fitted him only here and there into a Southern gentleman. "You're only a kid yourself," he told her, admiringly. "I bet you aren't any older than my sister Lizzie. She's pretty, too."

"Your sister!" the girl whispered. The red-papered hall was very still as the girl in the short gold dress stared at young Lee; then suddenly her lips quivered and he had no way of knowing what she was thinking. She flung up her chin and said too shrilly, "Boy, you're so skinny you have to look twice to see you're there! Here." She drew something from the bosom of her dress and tossed it to him, ordering, "For cripes' sake, go buy yourself a square meal, *hombre!*"

When he got outside and looked under the street lamp, she'd given him a five-dollar bill! And the feel of it was still warm from her breast. Lee had never held so much money in his hand before; it awed him. But he was so hungry. . . . That night the Nies family had the thick, juicy steak Lee had been dreaming of for weeks; but he lied to his mother; he told her he'd found some money. But hadn't his mother lied, too, about the girl? Lee figured. How could she be bad when she'd done that for him?

His ignorance did not last long; but the truth young Lee discovered there in the red-papered hallway was to be of more use to him than his college degrees; it was to run like a cleansing stream through all his life, making him understand all men and women who sinned and were kind, who had in them both the spider and the butterfly fighting for control. The truth Lee learned for himself was the one he told the traveling salesman. "Nobody's all good or all bad; they're both—like me."

Lee worked for nine years, each new job paying a little better than the last, until he was "boss" of a spice mill with workers much older than himself under him; and as the mill's receipts went up, the owner raised Lee's salary. Soon, he figured, he'd be able to pay off the mortgage on their house, and set himself up in a business that would grow as Texas itself was growing. Then suddenly one day Lee found something he wanted more than money. At eighteen he threw up his job and went back to school!

This change in values was due to the Methodist minister. Lee's mother had been frantic because for the first time she hadn't been able to scrape up the quarterly payment for the bank. Mary Elizabeth had been sick, which meant not only the loss of her wages but doctor bills; the roof simply had to be fixed; and both boys had gone through their shoes. Lee's English was better than hers, so Bowitt took him with her to the bank when she went to explain that they could pay the remaining fifty dollars that was due within a few weeks. Surely there would be no trouble, she reassured herself anxiously, since the banker was also a teacher in the Methodist Sunday school where the children went.

But she stumbled from nervousness as she went up the bank steps, so that Lee caught her arm, and felt, shocked, how thin she was. Yet for all her thinness there was still strength in her, and grace; she walked straight and slim across the bank floor as if she were going down a furrow in her bare feet; yes, his mother had the strength of the good brown earth in her.

But when Bowitt asked the banker for more time, he flatly refused. "After all," he reminded her smugly, "the bank owes something to its depositors. A widow with so many children is not —forgive me—a very good risk."

"Do you not see me in church every Sunday? Would I lie to you? I tell you, in a few weeks. . . ." Bowitt's voice broke as she shredded her handkerchief with her fingers, already seeing her children without shelter, all the long days of her toil gone for nothing.

The banker leaned closer. "Because you are a good woman and I would like to help you, I will buy your house from you myself," he offered. "At a fair price, of course."

Lee watched the banker's tongue flicker froglike out over his lips. "No," he said, his boy's voice cracking with anger and embarrassment. "We will not sell." He hustled his mother out of there, she protesting tearfully that fifty dollars did not grow on trees and now he had made an enemy of that man who could turn them out of their home! Lee told his mother, "I don't trust him, Ma. I know he wouldn't pay what the house is worth."

"But what can we do?" his mother wailed.

"Is anything the matter, my friends?" a voice asked behind them as they stood arguing on the sidewalk.

It was the minister from their church, the Dallas Tabernacle. He wore a Prince Albert coat, shiny and worn at the lapels with a greenish cast to the black cloth, but there was a jaunty tilt to the big tan hat on his head. One of the things which Lee liked best about this man was the way he made it seem such a joyous thing to serve the Lord. But when Bowitt explained what had happened, the minister's face grew grave.

"I have just been paid for the month," he told them. "It is just the amount we need." "We need." Lee stood staring, a thickness in his throat as the minister emptied his pocket, counting out fifty dollars into Bowitt's water-wrinkled hand. Young Lee said huskily, "I'll pay you back. I swear I will."

"Of course. Any time. I think," the minister said grimly, tucking his hand inside Bowitt's arm, "that I'll just go inside with you to be sure you get a proper receipt from our brother. Besides, I'd like a word with him. After you, Mrs. Nies."

As the minister handed his shabbily dressed mother back up the bank steps as if she were a great lady, Lee all but worshiped his disappearing coattails. This man was not afraid of anyone! He could look his richest parishioner in the eye, and tell him he had sinned! To the boy standing there in his patched pants with his

lanky wrists hanging out of his too-short shirt sleeves, it seemed
that to do what the minister had done for his mother this morning,
to give her not only money but to hand her back her self-respect,
was a bigger job even than being President of these United States.

What was it his father had said as he hammered his shoes so long
ago in his shop? "To be free to choose and to choose God's way
is all that makes us different from the animals." Suddenly Lee
knew what he wanted to do with the long years ahead of him: he
would go back to school; he would go to college; he would be a
minister. That he had no money, no backing, and the best colleges
were thousands of miles away, back East, did not bother him;
you made up your mind what you wanted to do and then did it.

It is doubtful if Bowitt would have agreed to Lee's going back to
school just as he was about to earn a man's salary, except to prepare for the ministry. To her mind it was a great thing, balm to
her battered pride, to think that she, who had stood at her tubs
so many years, should have a son in the pulpit. She wished that
her George were here to know about it—*their* son, standing up in
the pulpit and all the other people sitting silent, listening to what
Lee said!

It was not easy to go back to the fourth grade at eighteen,
doubling up your knees to get them under the too-small desk,
listening to some little girl spell better than you. Lee worked nights
at the spice mill to make expenses, getting home at five in the
morning; by nine he had to be at school, but he rigged a pin in
his seat in such a way that if he slouched and started to go to
sleep, it would prick him awake.

Lee's older brother, George, had moved to Fort Worth some
years earlier and had married Dora Blandin. They lived directly
across the street from Dora's sister, Susan Rouse, and her family,
who were thus vaguely "kinfolks" to Lee. When Lee finished
grammar school in two years, Dora suggested that if he wanted to
go on studying at Texas Wesleyan College in Fort Worth he
could help her with the housework for his board. Lee swept,
cleaned, and baby-sat with a Latin book in one hand. (T.W.C.
at that time prepared for the best universities, but was not a full-
fledged, degree-granting college.) Lee worked out math problems

on the top of the wooden kitchen table and then scoured them off. He won three medals for excellence in his studies those two years; he also found time in the small hours of the morning to read the theological books his minister in Dallas had loaned him, so Lee could apply for admission to the Austin Methodist Conference.

At night Lee was often kept awake by the laughter on the wide front porch across the street, for Isaac and Susan Rouse had three daughters who entertained half the male population of Fort Worth, it seemed. Myrtie, the eldest, had had her picture in the paper when she'd modeled at the Fair for a local jeweler, with the caption underneath, "THE PRETTIEST GIRL IN FORT WORTH." But to Lee she was just Myrtie, with whom he had played since she was six and he seven, when he built her a playhouse in the chinaberry tree in her back yard.

"Turn around while I climb up!" she had ordered Lee, for cowboys wore dungarees then, not ladies. "Now come on up, sugar, and I'll give you coffee in Pa's mustache cup!"

Lee rode to Texas Wesleyan with the three girls in their horse and buggy, but he usually managed to sit next to Myrtie.

How can I put into words the evanescent charm that was Myrtie Rouse at seventeen? She was small; her halo of short brown curls came only as high as Lee's topcoat button; and her blue eyes had that "come hither" look. She was more than pretty; if she'd had buck teeth and adenoids she still would have had that indescribable quality which the French call *je ne sais quoi*. From the time she was teething until she was seventy she had only to flirt her long dark lashes at any man, her wide mouth breaking into a smile of breathless wonder at what a great he-man he was—and there wasn't a male living who could say her nay. And besides all her other charms, she was kind.

Lee won the gold medal for "general proficiency" at Texas Wesleyan on the same day Myrtie won hers for excellence in playing Beethoven's *Moonlight Sonata* on the piano. Lee had never before owned anything of value, so he pinned it proudly upon his coat lapel. One of the straight-laced professors noticed Lee's decoration and motioned him aside—and when Lee went back to class his face was burning and the medal had disappeared.

"What did the old galoot say?" Myrtie murmured from her seat next to Lee's.

In his agony Lee blurted it out. "He said I was vulgar and ostentatious. *He told me to act like a gentleman, anyway.*"

"Is that so?" Myrtie snapped. Insult her kinfolks, would he? She reached into her handbag for her own small red-velvet box, and pinned her medal defiantly to her ruffled white shirtwaist. "Then I'm no lady!" she giggled. "Put yours right back on, sugar!" And thus they paraded, laughing, out of school, together.

He knew then, passionately, how he loved her; but how could she possibly feel the same way about him? She the prettiest girl in Fort Worth, and he a long, lanky crane, with no money at all and with years of study ahead of him before he earned any more? Yet he couldn't stay away from her. Evening after evening he would join the gang on the front veranda, singing the love he dared not say, accompanying himself on a banjo he'd bought cheaply because one of its strings was cotton. But his tenor voice was rich, true in pitch, blending sweetly with Myrtie's flutelike soprano. So they would sit very close together in the hammock, swinging and singing in the soft Texas dusk. Most of their courting songs seem to have been for deceased children.

"Close the shutters, Willy's dead," Myrtie would flute.

"Hope for him is fled," punk, punk, the cotton string would thump as Lee answered; and then they would wail happily together:

> *"From our home now sad and lone. . . .*
> *Close the shutters, Willy's dead."*

Lee had recently been appointed a local preacher in charge of a small mission in Dallas, so on Sunday nights he would drive Myrtie over in her own carriage to play the organ for him. Often they would put on "sacred concerts" standing there together in front of the congregation, warbling their mating songs without embarrassment. "Flee as a bird to its mountain," Myrtie's high soprano would invite, and Lee would answer, "Thou who are weary of sin. . . ."

It was obvious to the dullest in the parish that Myrtie could flee to Lee's mountain any time she wanted to; but he wasn't sure she would until that spring evening when they were driving back to Fort Worth after the service. The clop of the old mare's hoofs measuring off the long, enchanted miles couldn't go too slowly for Lee; and Myrtie's hair close to his cheek smelled like the magnolias they were passing, dimly white in the soft Texas night. He asked her for her picture to put into the back of the gold watch he'd won that week at T.W.C. as first prize for oratory. When Myrtie dug her picture out of her handbag where she'd carried it for weeks, hoping for this moment, Lee finally screwed up enough courage to ask if she could ever love him.

"Why, of course I'll marry you!" Myrtie cried. "I thought you'd never ask me!"

Worlds exploded and stars sang as he kissed his love for the first time. All Lee could think of that was big enough, grand enough to express how he felt, was the chorus from Handel's *Messiah* which the two of them had sung last Christmas in the college choir. "Hallelujah! Hallelujah!" his golden voice rang out over the dark, fragrant prairie, filling the startled night with exultant sound. But he was more than a young chanticleer arousing the Texas dawn to share his joy; he meant, he said, that there would be something holy about their life together. Myrtie cried happily and he kissed her again. They sang together all the way home, astonishing the sleeping farms.

And so they were engaged. "It's going to be a long pull—four years of college and then three at theological school," Lee worried. "I want to go to Evanston and then on to Boston. I need the best training I can get to find out God's way for me and for the world!" His voice shook. "But how can we possibly wait that long to be married?"

"I'll be waiting for *you*," Myrtie told him proudly.

Even then she could sense the goodness and greatness of the man he was to become. She felt dimly that Lee had something the other boys who came to her front veranda did not have, a restless, searching eagerness for living each day to the full. *He was looking for something bigger than himself, to find God's way.* What this meant she was not quite sure, nor did she greatly care. She knew simply that Lee was going to be a great man and that he was hers.

From then on nothing could have stopped Lee: there were no limits to his horizon, and no girl but Myrtie. That September the son of a shoemaker and a washerwoman set himself to get a college education at Northwestern University. He knew no one in Illinois, and had only his train fare, his tuition, and ten dollars in his pocket; but Myrtie's picture was in the back of his watch and the stars and stripes were in his eyes. Wasn't this young America, 1889? Wasn't he a citizen born? It never even occurred to Lee that he might fail.

CHAPTER 3

A White Church on a Hill

BOWITT HAD BY NOW hung up her tubs, for all her children had excellent jobs. Mary Elizabeth and Annie had opened a hat shop of their own which rapidly became so fashionable in the growing city of Dallas that "The Girls," as all the family and friends called them, began making trips to New York for samples and were even talking about Paris. The family could have afforded for Lee to be relieved of sending money home and to be required only to finance his own college education, a fair-sized job for any lad. But Bowitt's fear of losing her home had become an obsession; and she clung to the old-country idea that each child *owed* her his wages.

Another Old World insistence was that no child of hers should marry without her consent; but, when asked, she invariably found something wrong with each candidate for the Nies family. Mary Elizabeth, a warm-eyed, brown-haired girl with lusciously rounded curves made for love, had many beaux, and even slender black-eyed Annie had her chances. But the boys who called one evening would be vivisected mercilessly next morning along with the breakfast bacon by Bowitt's sharp tongue, reminding The Girls that without her backbreaking years at the ironing board, they

25

would hardly be there at all. So The Girls sublimated their longing for a home of their own by throwing themselves into their millinery business. No one who was anyone in Dallas would dream of buying a new hat without at least consulting "Miss Annie" or "Miss Lizzie."

But Lee was Bowitt's own son, his stubbornness matching hers. When he told his mother the day before he left for college that he and Myrtie were in love and intended someday to marry, Bowitt flew into a terrible rage.

"That little flibberty!" Bowitt cried. "Why, she hasn't the backbone of a—a moth! She can sing, ja. But life is no song, take it from me who knows. Has Myrtie ever done a hard day's work in her life? What kind of a minister's wife will she make? All the men will be making eyes at her!"

"You can't talk that way about Myrtie, even if you are my mother," Lee protested, a little muscle twitching in his cheek. "Myrtie's going to college too. To Ohio Northern in Ada, so she'll be able to help me better in the parish. I'll send you money every month. But when I get ready, I'm going to marry Myrtie Rouse. This isn't Neu-Isenburg. It's Dallas, Texas."

The look on her young son's face warned Bowitt to say no more; but she knew Lee loved her as she did him, in her own stern way; so she merely bided her time. If she really needed him, she knew in her heart that her son would come to her.

At first Lee found his college studies at Evanston much harder than he expected, for his preparation had been sketchier than most freshmen's.

The picture of Lee taken at college for Myrtie's dresser shows mostly a high white collar, over which peers a thin, eager face, with a candid brow, light hair parted in the middle, and hungry eyes. He was starved, not only for sleep and proper food, but for affection. The bitter penury of his life up to now had left him not only with rheumatism in his wrists and ankles, but with deep attacks of depression he found it hard to throw off.

"When I was studying last night, all of a sudden the words didn't make sense any more," he wrote once to Myrtie. "I guess I was just overtired. Don't worry, I'm all right."

It never occurred to him to go to a doctor. Waste good cash unless you were sick enough to be in bed? A broken leg, a pain in the belly maybe justified medical attention, but an overwrought nervous system—ach, dumbhead! as his mother would say. So Lee continued to cheat nature which merely piles up bills for future payment, by studying, running an eating business by day to support himself, and going all over Chicago and its suburbs by night to sing with the college quartet at innumerable Sunday-evening church services.

Lee was just finishing the first semester of his junior year at college when he received a letter from his mother begging him to come home at once. Their home was at stake, she wrote; maybe they would lose it entirely through some legal technicality she couldn't even understand. If Lee loved her, if he had any gratitude at all, he would take the next train to Texas.

When Lee arrived, he found the problem was indeed involved. Dallas had grown up around their little house until it was now in the business section, a valuable property. A purchaser insisted that Bowitt had agreed to sell him her house and land for $25,000, a vast sum to her; but Bowitt protested that she had merely discussed the matter with him, and had made no binding agreement. The would-be purchaser brought suit, knowing as Bowitt did not that the Magnolia Oil Company was looking for downtown land upon which to build and that the new City Hall was to be erected across the street from the Nies house. The suit dragged on, so Lee decided he must stay by his mother.

Two other factors kept Lee in Dallas. He was appointed to conduct the East Branch Mission of the Dallas Tabernacle, an offshoot of his old church where he had grown up. Of course Myrtie was the big reason he hated to leave Texas again, even for college. To Lee Myrtie represented all that he so fiercely craved, warmth, beauty, and the gentle courtesy that life had so far denied him. For sixty years from the playhouse in the chinaberry tree on, he was to give her a love such as few women know, as deep as his passionate nature and as high as eternity, for he said that if Myrtie wasn't there, he didn't want to go to heaven. It wouldn't be heaven anyway.

Lee's little church was near the neighborhood where he used to deliver telegrams, and some of the nearby saloons were not pleased to hear hymns seeping in through their swinging doors. One evening a gang buoyed up by a few drinks decided to break up Lee's service. Myrtie, at the organ, cast Lee an anxious glance as she saw the burly men crowding into the unaccustomed church seats, but he hissed at her, "Play 'Onward Christian Soldiers' loudly as you can!"

Myrtie opened up all the organ stops, for she knew as well as Lee that if they could get the whole gang singing, they'd forget the mischief they were so obviously bent upon. But all the newcomers did was to shuffle their feet, louder and louder, till the racket nearly drowned out the singing. Somehow, Lee knew desperately, he had to get and hold their attention before it was too late. He abandoned the text he had chosen for tonight and banged resolutely upon the pulpit for attention.

"Tonight I will discuss 'What's Wrong with Dallas?'" Lee shouted. "I used to deliver telegrams in this neighborhood, so I know it as well as any of you." He told the story of how he'd seen the Greaser murdered in a nearby saloon, while gradually the church became so still you could hear the street noises from outside coming in the open window. Lee kept the crowd of uneasy newcomers under his eye as he insisted, "What we need here, even now, is not just freedom, but *freedom within the law*. If Dallas is to become the great lady she may be, she must clean house!"

The crowd from the bar were too interested in listening to what Lee had to say to make any trouble. After the service the leader of the rowdies rushed up to Lee to shake his hand. "By God, you're just what this place needs—someone to speak out!" he cried.

"Drop in again and we'll talk it over," the wily Lee invited.

The leader came, and brought his friends, long, lean cattlemen who'd never been inside a church before, but who loved their home city. They came to understand that Lee's church meant not tearing down, but progress. The man who'd come to make trouble, his piety so new you could smell the varnish, became president of

their discussion group on Sunday mornings. Before the year was
out Lee had added 120 new names to the Mission membership roll,
making 200 members in all for his little new church. He might
have stayed there in Dallas if it hadn't been for Myrtie.

"Lee," she said one night, "I thought you said the best school
of theology in the country was in Boston? Have you given up going there?"

"You want to get rid of me?" Lee asked, hurt.

"I want you to be the big man I know you can be," Myrtie
told him. "How can you be bishop if you haven't even graduated
from college?"

Lee scoffed at the bishop fantasy, but he wrote to Boston University and was accepted. The suit had gone against his mother,
so she had had to sell the house after all; at least she thought she
had to, though actually under Texas law no one could compel the
sale of a homestead such as hers. Bowitt never was to cease bewailing her loss, but Lee was inwardly relieved that the mess was
over. Money in itself was never to be very important to him. That
fall he kissed his love good-by and set out for book-learned Massachusetts, a raw Texas youth whose girl was sure he would learn
in the Athens of Boston how to be a bishop.

In Boston for the first time Lee had trouble earning money.
He had stuffed the post cards Myrtie sent him into the holes in
the soles of his Sunday shoes when by sheer chance he got the
opportunity to supply the little white church in Townsend.

"Lee, do you want a job preaching upstate next Sunday morning?" one of the older theological students asked him at breakfast
one morning. "Place called Townsend that pays five bucks. I said
I'd go, but now I've got another bid from a church that pays ten!"

"You bet I'll go," Lee agreed hastily. He inspected the contents
of his pocket anxiously. "How much does it cost to get there?"
He was to go on Saturday, and board through Sunday at a woman's
called "Aggie Going." At least he would eat this week end.

Lee didn't like Boston very well, because after the wide Texas
prairies the city's little crooked streets shut him in so he could
hardly breathe. But the fussy little train he took from the North

Station that Saturday afternoon was fun; the train had only two cars with no water cooler, so that the conductor came around with a teakettle and a dipper to offer the thirsty a drink. As they left the city behind, the rolling meadows and rocky rises were fringed with dark, pointed pines. Because it was late May, every now and then a flowering bush in full glory, white, pink, or yellow, would be splashed breathtakingly against the gray granite rocks. When Lee got off the train at Townsend he imagined he could even smell apple blossoms! He walked up the street, sniffing spring; and then he looked up and caught his breath. There on the top of a little wooded hill, with its tower pointing like the finger of God up, up into the never-ending sky, stood an old white church.

And what a lovely church! Here were no hampering horizons, for the ancient clean-lined building stood so high it seemed to float in the blue sky-sea. Later Lee learned that the tower was a copy of one designed by the great architect Christopher Wren; but now Lee knew only that this house of God was beautiful, and that walking up the steep little hill through the avenue of pines to the open front door was like coming home.

"I wish Myrtie could see this," Lee thought. "I wish we could be married here at this ancient altar where for so many years people have knelt to pray." It seemed to him as if all the babies who had been baptized here, all the brides and grooms who had said so hopefully, "I do!", all the coffins that had lain here at the altar to be blessed and then had gone out empty because the souls who had left them were ranging the lovely purple hills of Townsend on their way to another heaven, had left behind the incense of holiness. Lee preached as he never had before, a hymn of worship and thanksgiving—and after the service, he was startled when the church official members asked him to be their supply preacher every Sunday!

"I already have a church job!" he wrote Myrtie excitedly that night. "At ten dollars a week. At least, I get five in cash and they board and room me from Saturday through Sunday afternoon. The church is over a hundred years old; it even has a slave pew in back where the black servants of the old Puritans (did you know they had slaves?) used to sit, with just a slit to look through so they could see but not be seen! All the color prejudice wasn't in the South!"

But what Lee liked best about the white church was its great bell that went booming among the little crooked hills every Sunday morning, a mighty voice calling to worship. It was the biggest bell cast up to then in Boston when it was brought to Townsend by oxcart years ago, so that the whole side of the tower had to be taken down to get it inside. The chairman of the White Church board wanted a bell bigger that that of the Brick Church situated down the hill and across the village common, which the White Church members called smugly, "Down the Other Way." But the new bell was so huge that there was some question as to whether it was safe to ring it, lest the vibrations weaken the church tower. That first Sunday everyone held his breath while the sexton gingerly pulled the bell rope, then harder and harder.

"Boom," came the voice of the great bell. "*Boom. Boom!*"

And the tower didn't even shake. The board chairman wiped the nervous perspiration from his forehead and said happily, "Listen to her! I bet they can hear *her* 'Down the Other Way!'"

Lee did not approve of the rivalry between the two churches; he thought they should pull together; so the first chance he got, he went down the hill to call on the older pastor of the Brick Church. The minister handed Lee a town report with the names of all the voters, saying coldly, "Mark off your members. All the rest of the town belongs to me." There wasn't much a very young man could do to combat such an attitude, so Lee wrote Myrtie he guessed he'd tend to his own knitting.

Lee always said that that first real New England congregation of his preached him more sermons than he did them. Certainly he learned a great deal about human nature not written in textbooks. Since his parish was scattered on farms among the hills, he rented a bicycle and visited all day every Saturday. His unannounced arrival frequently got him into embarrassing situations. One afternoon he knocked at the open door of a lonely farmhouse where an old man was sitting at the kitchen table, playing solitaire.

"You play seven up?" he demanded hopefully of Lee.

"No, I'm afraid not," he admitted.

"What about poker?"

"No. . . ."

"Well, what in tarnation can you do, young feller?" the old man was demanding when his daughter came in from gathering eggs. "Why, Pa!" she gasped, "that's the new Methodist minister, come to call!"

They all three laughed so hard that the old man came to church next Sunday for the first time in ten years and put a dollar bill into the collection plate. He continued to do this as long as Lee was there, for he said that he wanted to hear a minister who could laugh at himself. The congregation picked up considerably after Lee's calls, and because, as Aggie Going, at whose home he boarded week ends, said, Lee's Southern voice would wheedle a bee out of its hive.

Aggie was a darling, Lee wrote Myrtie, a mere little scrap of a woman with a tongue that had a sharp New England twang; but she was the best cook he'd ever eaten after, and her heart was bigger than all Texas. She told Lee that if the collection any Sunday wasn't enough to pay his salary, he was not to go hungry the rest of the week; she always had something tucked away in her tea-pot for emergencies. "She meant it too," Lee assured Myrtie.

Aggie Going's great grief was that her husband Charles was not a member of her church. What was more, he shocked the orthodox in town by saying he didn't believe in God anyway; that prayer was merely man bucking himself up. But Charles Going was a jolly man, popular with the young fry in town just feeling their oats and ripe for talking back to their elders, who hung out in gangs at Charles's store. He backed them up in their green-apple independence and was responsible for not a few of them leaving the church and Sunday school.

One Sunday Lee hired Charles with his horse and buggy to take him to the neighboring town where Lee was to preach; and because he had to wait anyway, Charles came inside the church to hear what this young squirt had to say. Lee spoke on "Immortality and You," saying that God wouldn't be the one to keep us out of heaven; it would be our own misdeeds which would make us so uncomfortable we couldn't stay near Absolute Purity, even if our own loved ones were there.

On the way home Charles asked young Lee, "Did you mean what you said this morning? That Aggie and I might be separated for all eternity because we believe differently?"

Lee glanced at him curiously and answered with another question. "Charles, how can you say there is no God when you don't give yourself a chance to know Him?"

"How can you know an invisible, nonexistent God?" Charles spat scornfully.

" 'If any man will do His will, he shall know of the doctrine, whether it be of God,' " Lee quoted. "Are you doing God's will as well as you know it, Charles?"

"You know darn well I'm not," Charles told Lee. "But I tell you what I'll do. I'll try this thing out—but for Aggie's sake, you understand; not because of anything you've said."

The first thing Charles did when they got home was to go to apologize to someone he'd called "a liar" before the gang in his store. When he came back home, he announced to his startled family, "If I'm going to find out what God wants me to do, we'd better have family prayers. Mr. Nies, you lead this first time, but tomorrow I'll take over—not that I'm really talking to anyone, of course; but I'll give this a fair trial."

Charles told the boys in his store frankly what he was doing and urged them to go to church just as he was, to see what the minister said, but the boys just laughed at him. "You know this is only a stunt, Charles," they said. It worried Charles, who said to Lee, "Suppose I have led them to a barren pasture?"

A few months later Charles came home early from cutting pine in his wood lot, saying that he felt terrible. The doctor put him to bed, warning that the angry red spot spreading over his face was erysipelas and dangerous to fool with. When Lee got to Townsend that week end, Aggie met him at the door, sobbing that Charles was going to die and wanted Lee to pray with him. The red, swollen man on the bed was almost unrecognizable, but when Lee got up from his knees, Charles's familiar voice said, "You forgot something, Mr. Nies."

"What was that?" Lee asked.

"*You forgot to ask God to forgive my sins—for Jesus' sake.*" Charles's swollen hands twisted on the bedspread as he said, "I've spent forty years going in the wrong direction. And I've hauled other folks with me. I don't need justice. What I need is a Saviour!"

"The whole world needs Him too, not just you, Charles," Lee told him. " 'There is none other name under heaven . . . whereby we must be saved.' *He's right here now.*"

The light that never was shone upon Charles's tortured face as he gasped, "I know He is! I've done His will and now I know. There's something I want you to do for me, Lee." He called the minister by his first name for the first time as he begged, "I want you to get up at my funeral and tell them that I'm sorry for the bad influence I've had on this town, on the young people who came to my store. I want you to tell them that God's a bigger man than I am—that he's forgiven me, for Jesus' sake."

Both mills in town closed for the funeral, and the church couldn't hold all the people who wanted to get inside. Lee wrote to Myrtie, "When I got up to tell them what Charles wanted me to, the crowd was so moved, they were like a forest of trees bowed by a storm. I could hardly speak, myself. But the glory of God was in that church."

Shortly after Charles went away, a telegram came for Lee which shook his complacent world to pieces. "Myrtie badly injured Crystal Palace fire but not burned," it read. "Thought you might see casualty lists in paper. Letter follows. Susan Rouse."

"A paper! I've got to have a newspaper!" Lee shouted, and Aggie rushed to thrust the evening paper into his hand, but it shook so that he could hardly read. The story was there on the front page about the Crystal Palace's burning, but Lee knew already from Myrtie's letters about its being built in Fort Worth to exhibit Texas products, wheat, corn, and cotton. Someone must have dropped a match and the whole place burned in a matter of minutes, the headlines screamed. Scores had been badly burned or hurt. Lee shuddered, reading Myrtie's name among them. Two days of torment followed until he got Susan Rouse's letter with details. Myrtie had been running out down the main staircase; the crowd had stampeded at the terrible cry, "Fire!" and the stairway collapsed. A man grabbed Myrtie and hauled her outside. When she came back to consciousness Myrtie found herself lying in a strange man's arms, with no clothes left on her except her steel-ribbed corset and her stockings!

"The shock did something to her eyesight," her mother wrote. "The doctor calls it hysteria, and says she'll see as well as ever when she gets over this, but he thinks she should have a change of scenery. She grieves she can't see to write you herself but she sends you her dear love. . . ."

Myrtie almost blind and needing you. . . .

Seeing the horror on Lee's face, Aggie took the letter from his shaking hand and read through to the end. "Well, you just got to go right home, Lee, marry that girl, and bring her back here," Aggie said briskly. "You can live on the ten dollars a week cash that we raised your salary to last month, if we get you a parsonage to live in. I've done it plenty. The church furniture's all scattered, but I guess we can gather it up."

Lee picked up the little woman and kissed her. "Aggie," he cried, "did I ever happen to mention that I love you?"

The furniture was scattered, all right. One family had been using the black iron stove for years and gave it up reluctantly; another family was eating off the dining-room table; and some of the chairs were being used by the village undertaker to save storage on them. Lee hired a wagon and gathered up everything he could find and took them to the new little white parsonage the church had rented for eight dollars a month, whose veranda looked out upon the rows of gray and white stones in the cemetery. Lee had had the choice of a house facing the hearse-house or the cemetery, and had chosen the latter as he thought Myrtie would like the neighbors better. The Ladies' Aid dug up some rag rugs and curtains. The house looked fine to Lee, but he had a hunch that Myrtie would like to change things around.

Myrtie and Lee were married on September 25, 1894, in the Rouse's big, comfortable front parlor. (Her eyes were suddenly cured when they saw Lee.) The house overflowed with wedding presents, for Isaac was city alderman and official member of the

St. Paul's Methodist Church, but the only gift that came from
Lee's side of the family was a silver-plated pie knife from his
sister Carrie. Bowitt was bitterly angry that Lee had chosen to go
against her wishes, so none of the Nies family dared come to the
wedding. But Myrtie cherished the pie knife long after its silver
had worn off, and she always spoke to Lee of Carrie as "your
sister who stood by us."

It wasn't until they were together on the train, heading for
Niagara Falls, that Lee fully realized that Myrtie was actually his
at long last. He looked at her new finery, at her hair curling in
little ringlets so close to his mouth as they sat demurely on the
red Pullman seats, trying not to look like bride and groom. Suddenly he was a little afraid. What if he shouldn't be able to take
care of Myrtie after all? Ten dollars a week wasn't much for a
girl who was used to everything. His mother had been right about
one thing: Myrtie had never done a hard day's work in her life.
Myrtie's blue eyes met his scared blue ones.

"Turn your back, Lee, till I climb up," she murmured, smiling
up at him under long eyelashes. "You want me to get you some
coffee in Pa's mustache cup, sugar?"

She understood as she always did; she was inviting him again
to keep house in her chinaberry tree, reminding him she was the
same Myrtie he'd loved as a child. "All tickets, please!" the conductor called. "Bless my soul!" He passed the two of them by for the
time being, chuckling, for he'd never seen a girl being kissed as
thoroughly as Myrtie was.

As they neared Niagara Falls, Lee was worried about money,
though he'd rather die than tell Myrtie so. The advance he'd borrowed ahead on his salary had melted alarmingly. After a hasty
checkup of the cash in his pocket when he went to the washroom,
Lee ordered only coffee and rolls for his breakfast in the diner.
Myrtie had grapefruit, cereal, bacon and eggs, and an extra cup of
coffee which Lee hated himself for checking off mentally on the
menu price list. What kind of husband were you to begrudge your
lovely bride her food? But when you had only six dollars and
eighty-nine cents left . . .

The big hotel to which the taxi man took them had a red-plush carpet you sank in to your ankles and much gilt furniture. Myrtie flirted her eyelashes at the room clerk, murmuring, "You'll give us a nice front room, won't you? Where we can see the Falls?"

"How much do rooms cost?" Lee asked, hastily.

"Ten dollars for front and five for back," the clerk said, bored with all brides and grooms. "Or twenty-five for the bridal suite— a day," he added as Lee's eyes widened. The clerk looked even more scornful as Lee suggested with perspiration on his forehead, "Sugar, the water makes an awful roar. We'll never sleep." He asked the clerk, "What about a nice back room? Rather—er— small."

"Naturally, if you can't afford a front one . . ." the clerk sneered in a tone that usually reduced the sweating groom into taking the larger room; but he'd reckoned without Myrtie. She might be thoughtless but she was certainly not disloyal; when she saw the blood rush to Lee's forehead, she understood. Her hand slid into her small white handbag and then into Lee's blue coat pocket.

"Sugar, why don't you change that fifty-dollar bill so I can buy a paper?" she asked Lee sweetly. Dazed, Lee put his hand into his pocket, drew it out, and miraculously the fifty dollars was really there, in his hand. Myrtie whirled on the room clerk, storming, "And as for you . . ." High-hat her Lee, would he? "I have kinfolks on the Texas Pacific Railroad that run this place, and I'm certainly goin' to tell them how no-account their help are!"

When the dazed Lee took her into his arms in their small back room, she was shaking all over. "Don't cry," he begged.

But Myrtie was laughing. "That room clerk looked so—so squashed!" she gasped. "Oh, Lee, I'm so sorry I was so dumb. But it *was* funny!"

"Where on earth did you get all that money?" Lee asked, awed.

"Pa gave it to me for pin money," Myrtie explained. She pressed her smooth young mouth against his, murmuring, "Oh, Lee, isn't it marvelous to be married? Alone, I mean, alone together!"

If she could laugh at a penniless husband, she had a good start toward being a good minister's wife, Lee thought ruefully as he held her close. They didn't go look at the Falls until morning.

CHAPTER 4

Honeymoon on Ten Dollars a Week

IT WAS FORTUNATE that Lee and Myrtie Nies had the lovely gift of laughter, and that as long as they were together, they could see the funny side of even poverty, parsonages, and pain. There are very few who can reach for life avidly with both hands and accept what they grasp, be it bloody and sharp, or smooth and gracious, without becoming bitter. Those who have this rare gift of enjoying each moment to the full do not lose their zest for living until the day they die; in a larger sense, their happiness never dies. For what else does it mean, the promise about heaven, that there shall be no tears there?

The bride and groom were met at the Townsend station and escorted to the new parsonage by a cordial delegation from the Ladies' Aid, bearing a large welcoming pillow of purple and white cosmos. Myrtie was thrilled with her flowers and watered them daily; but when finally they faded, Lee stared at the empty wire of the pillow. "Do you see what I see?" he asked Myrtie, unbelieving; and then both of them shouted with laughter. The wire spelled out the words AT REST. The thrifty New Englanders had retrieved the pillow from the grave of one of their recently deceased members and used it again to welcome the bride!

The village soon learned that the new minister's wife was more decorative than she was a good housekeeper. She stared helplessly at the big black iron wood stove, for at home there'd been a maid to do all the cooking and cleaning. The parsonage had no plumbing except for a cold-water faucet in the kitchen, and a place out in the woodshed which she and Lee called "Blueberry Inn." But she had plenty of time to learn to cook, as Lee went into Boston to the School of Theology five days a week. Myrtie would never forget making her first apple pie. She kneaded the dough for hours, trying to get it just right for Lee's supper, but the uncooperative mess kept sticking to the board; and when she finally put the pie into the oven, Myrtie burnt her hand. She was sucking her fingers and crying when the president of the Ladies' Aid came in the back door without knocking, in the friendly way people do in the country, calling out, "Anybody home?"

"Hel-lo!" Myrtie gasped, wiping her eyes and trying to smile. "I—I was making a pie." The president took one look at the flour that coated the kitchen floor, the walls, the stove, sniffed at the smell of something burning, yanked open the oven door, and snatched out the poor, leathery, lopsided pie.

"My grief, don't they teach you *anything* in Texas?" she demanded. And then her eyes nearly popped out of her head, staring at the beer bottle lying there on the bread board as if it had been a rattlesnake. "*Where did you get that thing?*" Myrtie told her that she'd picked it up on the dump because she didn't have a rolling pin. "We'd better get rid of it fast, if your husband wants to stay in this town!" the older woman said. "We'll use the ketchup bottle." She rolled up her sleeves and showed the quivering bride how to cut the lard delicately into the flour, and popped a real pie into the oven. Then the Ladies' Aider regarded prudently the bushel basket of beans under the table that one of the farmers in the church had brought to the parsonage that morning and said they'd taste a lot better if canned before sundown.

"But I don't know how," Myrtie confessed miserably. "And I haven't any cans!"

"Jars," the older woman corrected. Her glance added, "Heaven help your poor starving husband this winter!" But she brought back a dozen glass jars from her own house, set Myrtie to snapping the bushel of beans, and taught her the art of the hot-water bath for vegetables.

That summer happened to be a damp one and all the parish gardens were a riot of green beans. When they had too much of anything to sell, the farmers in the parish always donated some to the minister. "Conscience fodder" Lee called it, because it excused how little cash the givers put into the Sunday collection plate, but to Myrtie's Southern friendliness, the one unforgivable sin was to hurt anyone's feelings, so she never refused any offering. Beans continued to pour in at the parsonage in a green flood, so the dutiful Myrtie canned and canned. It was no picnic hanging over the hot wood stove on a summer day, but she "did up" sixty-five quarts, enough for Lee and her for years since neither of them liked beans very well, before she balked.

"I can't look another bean in the face!" she wailed to Lee. "And there's six more bushels of the horrible things down cellar. Oh, Lee, what are we going to do?"

He laughed and kissed her. "Bury them," he suggested. "With full ecclesiastical honors. By the light of the moon!"

Lee dug a long trench that night in the moonlight while Myrtie hung out the window alternately giggling and humming Chopin's funeral march. "Well, that's that!" And Lee stamped down the last spadeful of dirt over those telltale beans that his tenderhearted young wife hadn't been able to refuse. Only this wasn't the end, at all. The warm, damp weather continued, and one day Myrtie looked out the kitchen window. Lee came tearing down from his study when he heard her having hysterics; he shook her, but she couldn't stop laughing. All she could do was to point out the window to where those miserable beans were sprouting again out of the brown earth.

"Be sure your sins will find you out!" Lee gasped, between shouts of helpless laughter.

But even with the vegetables, chickens, and fruit the farmers brought in, Lee and Myrtie found living on ten dollars a week pretty tight going when his student ticket to Boston cost fifty cents a day. That left only seven-fifty a week for everything; and they religiously sent a dollar a month to Bowitt as Lee had promised to do.

They couldn't afford the $1.50 an afternoon for a horse and buggy so Lee and Myrtie rented two bicycles every week end and went together on their parish calls, over the lovely swelling hills to the scattered white farmhouses. Myrtie used to inspect her slim legs anxiously at night to be sure she wasn't getting ugly lumps of muscles like a circus rider.

Lee's singing was what really won their way into the hearts of his people, Myrtie used to chuckle when they reached home nights, weary but happy; that and the way he could make those squeaky old organs stand up and shout. Lee had never had a music lesson in his life, but if he heard anything once, he could play it perfectly by ear, on the organ, piano, banjo, violin, or "bull fiddle." He became in effect the poor man's radio, before even a crystal set was heard. When the parishioners saw him coming, they'd rush to start a fire in the front parlor stove which had been cold for months, and then cluster expectantly around the organ. Treading carefully over the best carpet, Lee would screw up the organ stool to the right height, pull out all the stops, throw back his yellow head, and begin, "There's an old rugged cross . . ." His rich tenor was contagious; pretty soon the wife would join in, then the children; even the old grandmother would hum and the farmer would nod his head and keep time with his heavy-shod foot. "Nearer my God, to thee," they'd sing, growing louder with each verse till the grand old hymn would roll out the window, over the greening hills, and far away.

The next Sunday morning the whole family, friends with the new minister, would be at church. The congregations grew and grew and when finally Lee organized the new quartet, the seats were filled even on Sunday evenings, an unheard-of occurrence. Tim Flaherty led the village band in its weekly concerts on the Common below the hill where the White Church stood. Lee talked him into playing the flute and another band player the violin; Myrtie was at the organ and Lee played the cello by ear (after Tim had showed him about the strings and where to press his fingers for the scales). They made sweet music. "Now every-

body just hum the next hymn," Lee would look up from his cello
to say, and the quartet would sink to a mere whisper of sound:

> *"One sweetly solemn thought*
> *Comes to me o'er and o'er. . . ."*

When the hymn finished, Auntie Gilson in the front seat would
be wiping her eyes, and she wasn't the only one. Maybe it wasn't
great music, but it was as natural as a bee humming around a
trumpet vine and the people loved it. Lee never bothered to go
down the steps from the choir to preach after the song service; his
long legs would just step over the low curtain to the pulpit and
he would talk to his farmer friends about how Jesus walked the
fields as they did; how He picked a lily of the field or stopped to
talk to a child.

"He's right here now," Lee would promise. "Waiting to talk to
your heart. Be still and listen." In that moment of silent prayer it
seemed to Myrtie as if the old church spoke God from every ancient
beam.

Auntie Gilson, who always sat up in the front seat, keeping her
eyes unwaveringly upon Lee from the depths of her old-fashioned
scoop bonnet, was a great satisfaction to him. Here was one person
who took to heart what he said, often being so moved that when
he finished a touching story there were tears in her eyes. But one
day Lee merely gave a résumé of church statistics and Auntie
Gilson still cried. When he shook hands with her at the front door,
Lee asked, curious, "Auntie, what was it I said today that touched
you so?"

"Oh, it wasn't anything you *said*," the old lady told him. "It's
just that you 'mind me so of my son Jimmy. He went when Mr.
Lincoln called him—but he never came back from that awful war."
She looked up at Lee. "Would you mind very much if I kissed you?
For Jimmy?"

Lee was just descending into the depths of Auntie Gilson's poke
bonnet when his bride of a few months discovered what was going
on. When the red-faced Lee explained, Myrtie patted Auntie
Gilson's black bombazine shoulder. "You can kiss my husband any
time you want to!"

Life was opening up for Lee like a wonderful flower; but he found that as well as a sweet scent, a rose could also house a bumble-bee with a nasty sting.

Lee had first met Sister Sears when she tipped him fifty cents for giving her his seat on the crowded Boston train. He naturally wouldn't sit while an old lady stood for the hour's train ride, but as she brushed by him at the terminal, Lee couldn't believe his eyes when he found she'd pressed a silver half dollar into his hand! When he went next Saturday up to the Sears farm to return the money he found out how Sister Sears got to be so odd. She'd had a baby son twenty years ago, she told Lee. He had been playing about the kitchen where she was washing; somehow the baby had tumbled into the scalding water and was burned so badly that he died.

"The Lord has punished me plenty," she told Lee bitterly, "for my carelessness."

"But the Lord isn't like that!" Lee protested. "He's a father too. . . ."

"Then how come I never had another baby?" she flared.

After Lee's visit, Sister Sears took a notion to the young bride and groom in the parsonage and adopted them into her own family. The first chickens were sent there, luscious strawberries, eggs when they were so expensive that Lee and Myrtie were afraid to even look at them in the grocery store, the best the farm had was shared with the parson and his wife; and Sister Sears never missed a Sunday at church. She and her sister sat right across the aisle from each other every week. Lee had been preaching a series of sermons on "Living with Your Neighbors," all about "the oil of politeness," kindliness, and the evils of gossip. All at once Sister Sears stopped coming to church. When she'd been missing for four Sundays in a row, even if it was snowy, cold December weather, Myrtie got worried.

"We simply must go find out what's wrong with Sister Sears," she told Lee. "She's been so good to us. Maybe she's sick."

The Sears farm was three miles away on the edge of "Loontown," and since they couldn't very well bicycle over ice and snow, Lee and Myrtie hired a sleigh out of their slender funds. The winter day was crisp and sunny and their spirits rose as the sleigh slipped over the creaky snow and the sleigh bells jingled; but they were nearly frozen by the time they reached the farm and rushed in through the shed, laughing and stamping the snow off their shoes. Sister Sears stopped them at the kitchen door, her face bleak, her eyes stony.

"Stop right where you be, you two!" she ordered. "You can't come inside here!"

She must be joking. Lee laughed heartily, reaching for her hand to pump it up and down. "My, but it's good to see you! You been sick?"

Sister Sears yanked her hand away as if Lee's fingers burned hers. "You git right out of here, you hypocrite! I don't know if your wife is a hypocrite too, but *you* are!"

Myrtie grew pale and Lee stammered, "But I don't understand. . . ." He looked behind the old lady to where Pa Sears, her husband, was shaving in the kitchen, and the old man motioned him violently in the mirror to go away. "There must be some mistake," Lee said quietly. "Come, Myrtie."

They worried all the way home about how they could have offended Sister Sears. The only thing they could think of was Myrtie's turkey soup. Someone had told her to boil the bones of their donated Thanksgiving turkey to make a fine soup; and when Sister Sears, chilled to the bone with her long ride from the farm, had stopped up at the parsonage with some turnips, Myrtie had warmed her up with the soup. Later Myrtie was horrified to find she hadn't boiled the bones long enough and the mess tasted like dirty dishwater. "But surely she wouldn't think I did it on purpose!" Myrtie wailed unhappily to Lee. "But these country people are so—so stone-quiet. You never can tell *what* they think." It was useless to conjecture; all they could do was pay out their precious $1.50 and walk home downcast from the livery stable.

The next morning Lee saw Pa Sears creak by in his old sleigh for the mail, so the worried young minister rushed over bareheaded to intercept him at the post office. Lee demanded, man to man, "What was wrong with your wife yesterday, Mr. Sears?"

The older man eyed him suspiciously. "You mean you really don't know?"

"I haven't an inkling," Lee insisted.

Pa Sears spat over the side of the sleigh. "Three or four weeks ago you preached a sermon on gossip." Lee nodded and the old man went on. "You bore down pretty hard on them that bore a grudge against their neighbors. Maybe you didn't know that my wife ain't spoke to her own sister for twenty-seven years!" Lee stared at him, speechless. But the two sisters sat right across the aisle from each other at church every Sunday morning! It didn't seem possible. "Quarreled over a quart of milk," Pa Sears explained. "Yes, sir, twenty-seven years ago come spring."

"I didn't know a thing about it," Lee told the old man, his young eyes flashing. "But if I had, I'd have 'borne down' harder than I did!"

Pa Sears regarded the young preacher with wise gray eyes as he remarked mildly, "I ain't a professed Christian, but I've put up with Ma for thirty years. Seems like you, a preacher, ought to be able to take it *once*. Giddap!" The sleigh slid away, leaving Lee standing there with his tail feathers drooping.

"I deserved what Pa Sears said, every word of it," Lee told Myrtie in the kitchen, all his righteous indignation having oozed out of him. "Will I ever remember 'Thy gentleness hath made me great'? Who am I to preach to anyone?"

It was a real thorn in the flesh that despite all his efforts, Sister Sears never came to church again as long as Lee was there. The empty pew preached silently to the young preacher, Sunday after Sunday, of his own unworthiness. It was a new lesson to him to hate the sin but love the sinner.

Lee was more successful with Aunt Betsey Fessenden, who'd already been fifty-two years in probationary membership when Lee came to the Townsend church. Her husband had owned the cooperage where nearly all the men in town worked, so it secretly irked her that *any* official board would dare to put her, Betsey Fessenden, *on probation!* Moreover, she wasn't quite sure she believed the Methodist Creed down to every comma. Lee convinced her that the creed wasn't as important as all Christian people working together, so, after half a century, Aunt Betsey finally came out of "probation" and into full membership. Her granddaughter Marion liked to laugh as well as Myrtie did, so the two became fast friends. When Marion was about to be married, the two girls chuckled for days when Myrtie discovered that the woman who lived across the street from the Fessendens' house was selling seats in her front windows for twenty-five cents apiece to people who weren't invited to the wedding!

Since he was not yet ordained deacon, under Massachusetts state law Lee could not perform a marriage ceremony; but he could baptize and bury his parishioners. His first baptism he would never forget. He did not want the congregation to know that he'd never baptized a baby before, so he accepted the infant casually in one arm and with his other hand held the baptismal cup, looking straight ahead while he exhorted the congregation loftily upon the meaning of holy baptism. But the congregation strangely didn't seem to be listening; broad smiles spread over face after face, and one of the teen-agers was giggling so that finally Lee looked down at the baby. The infant had seized the silver baptismal cup in both tiny hands and was drinking happily!

Lee referred his weddings to the older minister at the Brick Church, and gradually the two men, so dissimilar, came to understand each other. Once when Lee had been having special weekly meetings for deepening the spiritual life at the old White Church, many of the Red Brick Church young people attended, to the chagrin of their pastor. "I'm very grateful for your interesting them in religion," he told Lee stiffly. "But sorry they had to go to your church to find . . . reality. What do they get there that isn't in mine?"

Lee blushed. "Maybe a chance to express themselves," he suggested. "We talk over what it means to act a Christian, every day in the week."

The older scholar regarded the young Methodist exhorter doubtfully. "When you ask people to raise their hands for prayer and nobody does, what do you do? It would kill me if no one responded to my appeal!"

Lee's blue eyes held his as he said quietly, "You've got to be willing to be killed! For Christ's sake."

Thus the fresh eagerness of the young man tempered the conservative wisdom of the older minister, and the two of them became fast friends. The older man was much respected in the community, and when he was asked to speak, he frequently took Lee with him to meet the state leaders, socially and professionally. At one political meeting one old-timer began to attack "the foreign element which is creeping insidiously into our midst." The "foreign element" was merely a few industrious Finns who by working early and late had made a success of their farming and shamed some of the lazy descendants of the earlier settlers. The minister from the Brick Church listened to the tirade against these newcomers who were "taking the bread from honest men's mouths." When the speaker finally sat down, the wise old minister stood up, his eyes twinkling.

"What our friend says is true," he agreed. "These foreigners do worm their way into our chief places—even into our pulpits! There are two immigrants sitting right here on the platform tonight— myself and Mr. Nies. My family came from England and his from Germany!"

The audience laughed and cheered. In one minute the preacher had punctured an hour's discourse. Young Lee stored up in his memory the fact that quiet ridicule can be more effective than angry words. He learned much from this, as the older man himself had been humble enough to learn from Lee, a mere youngster.

Lee's first funeral was for a worker in the cooperage who'd hung himself in his own shed—greatly to everyone's surprise, for none had suspected his troubled state of mind. His own wife was so horrified that when Lee asked her what he should say at the funeral she cried bitterly, "He had no right to shame me and the children this way. The best thing he ever did was the last one!" Lee stayed awake all night wondering how he could best meet this shamed hurt so it would not always poison her memory of her husband. The church was filled when Lee stood up beside the closed coffin to speak the last farewell for a tortured soul.

"You highly regarded this man who worked beside you." He

swept his eyes along the pews of fellow workers from the cooperage. "But you didn't trouble to find out what burden he was carrying. If he'd had one friend who loved him, whom he could trust with his secret, this tragedy might never have happened. 'Am I my brother's keeper?'" As he paused the shamed glances of the sobered congregation slid across the closed coffin and then up to Lee's grave face. He ended simply, "Most of the burdens of the world would not grow overwhelming—if they were shared. There is small personal disgrace in the death of this man; all we his friends have died a little too." As the widow went out of the church, she wrung Lee's hand, sobbing, "Now the children can be proud of their Pa again!"

Lee lived in all his people's problems as intensely as in his own, and in the assurance of youth was much freer to offer advice than he ever was to be again. Olive, one of the girls in his church choir, fell in love with a slick young stranger who'd barely arrived in town before he volunteered to sing tenor and to take Olive back and forth from choir practice. Lee, who made it his business to interview the new singer, was suspicious of his smoothness. Finally he made the tenor admit he was already married.

"I don't care!" Olive wailed when Lee told her. "I love him and he loves me. He can get a divorce, can't he? If you won't marry us, then a justice of the peace will!"

Lee was sorely tempted to call her a "young fool," but the language did not sound exactly ministerial. Two days later when he was getting his mail, a poster upon the post-office wall attracted his eye. Startled, Lee called in the police chief and the young tenor left town rapidly in custody. He had already married three wives, relieved them of their cash, moved on (without bothering with a divorce) to court other girls, usually by joining a church, lodge, or some other stronghold of respectability. But even then Olive was not to be comforted. "I still love him!" she told Lee defiantly. "You can't understand a love as big as that, can you? I hate you for what you did to him!"

Six months later Olive was back at the parsonage with the boy who'd grown up next door to her. "I must have been crazy, Mr.

Nies," she admitted. "But now Jimmy here and I have found what love really means."

"Sometimes I feel like a mother hen that's hatched out ducklings." Lee grinned at Myrtie. "I cluck and cluck, but no one in the parish even listens. Doubtless they'd have learned to swim anyway, without my fuss."

"Sometimes I suspect that the biological urge is greatly overrated," Myrtie agreed absently, hauling her trousseau out of the closet to see if there was anything left fit to wear to Olive's wedding. "Oh, Lee, nothing will meet around my middle!" she wailed. "I'm getting fat!"

"Pleasingly plump," Lee corrected, ruffling her short hair. "You always smell good, sugar. Like sunshine in a pine grove. Or hot bread just out of the oven. A wind blowing over a hidden garden."

Should you tell him? Myrtie wondered, rubbing her cheek against his. Better wait until you are sure. . . .

The most fantastic experience that Lee had during his first pastorate at Townsend was undoubtedly Prissy Blake's funeral—which she conducted herself. His introduction to Prissy was equally startling. One afternoon when Lee was waiting for a funeral at the church to begin, while the relatives were saying farewell before the coffin lid was let down for the service, he noticed a woman in deep mourning come down the church aisle. But she didn't stay long. The undertaker flew at her like an angry hen, chasing her back up the aisle and out of the church!

"That ghoul!" the undertaker snorted to Lee when he came back, breathless. "Prissy Blake hasn't missed a funeral in these parts in ten years! Methodist, Baptist, Unitarian—it doesn't make any difference to her, so long's there's a corpse. There isn't any way to stop her hoverin' round either, short of making a fuss. But she knows I won't stand for her!"

But when Lee had finished the ceremony and stood waiting at the church door for the carriage to take him to the cemetery, there was Prissy Blake again, waiting with the rest of the mourners. But the undertaker edged up to her, saying sternly, "All the seats in the carriages are filled." Prissy gave him a long, cold look and melted away around the corner of the church. But when Lee got out at the cemetery, he saw Prissy alighting from the front seat of the hearse. "She'd hitchhiked with the corpse to the cemetery!" Lee gasped to Myrtie later. "Can you beat that?"

"She's crazy as a loon," Myrtie snapped. "I'm glad she doesn't belong to our church. It would scare me to sit back of her Sunday morning."

Lee saw Prissy Blake at many subsequent funerals, and came to accept her as an integral part of the ceremony like the undertaker; but it wasn't until May, the day before Myrtie's birthday, that he ever spoke to her face to face. It was a very stormy spring night with the wind lashing the tall elms above the small white parsonage, so that at first he didn't hear the knocker on the front door, and by the time he finally opened the door, Prissy was soaked through. She stood there in all her funeral rig, with her long wet black veil blowing out behind her in the wind.

"Come in, come in!" Lee urged. "I have a fire in my study where you can dry out."

He drew up a rocker in front of the round wood stove, raked up the embers, and added a piece of dry wood, so that the fire roared and crackled. Prissy turned back her wet skirt across her knees and flung back the widow's veil from her face, so that Lee could see the queer avid shining of her black eyes. Her face was long and triangular, with a perfect white skin; she'd have been a handsome woman if it hadn't been for her burning eyes. She fixed them now on Lee and asked, "Will you conduct my funeral tomorrow afternoon at two? At my house?"

"But—but—" stammered Lee, for certainly she looked very much alive.

Prissy grinned at him companionably. "It's my husband," she explained. "I guess you didn't even know I had one. Bill left me years ago. But tonight he came back. I could hardly believe my own eyes when I saw him standing there at my door, looking so skinny and awful white. 'Prissy,' he says, 'I'm a-dyin'. Can I come in?' "

The gleeful way she rolled the words under her tongue, savoring them, made Lee's blood run cold, for he realized that the wandering husband had known the only argument that would make Prissy let him in again under her snug roof—*she'd scented a funeral of her very own.*

"I put him on the couch in the parlor that's horsehair and don't show the dirt," Prissy rushed on. "I put a newspaper under his boots and covered him with a blanket. 'I'll get you some coffee, Bill,' I told him. But when I came back from the kitchen—" she drew a deep breath—"he was gone. I didn't need any doctor to tell *me*. So I tied up his chin like the undertaker would and put pennies on his eyes and came for you."

"No!" Lee said, staring at her with horror. "I couldn't possibly. . . ."

But Prissy didn't hear him. She got up and moved toward the front door, going right on as if Lee hadn't spoken. "Tomorrow at two at my house," she said. "I guess this is one funeral they can't throw me out of!" She flung open the door and strode out again into the storm, leaving Lee with his mouth still open to insist he wouldn't come.

But Myrtie didn't agree with him. "Someone has to bury the poor man, if only to be sure he's at rest and safe from Prissy from now on," she told Lee. "But if Prissy offers you any fee, don't take it. It'd be—blood money."

Reluctantly, Lee got into the carriage the undertaker sent the next day and rode to the white colonial house that sat on its greening lawn, surrounded by a neat white picket fence. Nearly every picket in the fence had a horse tied to it, for the road was crowded with every sort of vehicle, from a fashionable surrey to an empty hay wagon.

"Prissy's well connected in the county," the driver of Lee's carriage explained. Maybe that explained why she wasn't locked up in an asylum. Country people looked on insanity as merely another sickness; if the patient didn't harm anyone, leave him or her be. A shout of laughter greeted Lee as he walked in the front door and stood staring at the crowded front parlor where a long table loaded with ham, salad, and soft drinks had been pushed against the wall, where people were eating and chatting. Two men were even shaking hands over the closed casket which had been set up in the middle of the room. "Sam, by golly, I ain't set eyes on you for ten years!" one greeted the other cordially.

Great heavenly day, this was more like a church supper than a funeral, Lee was thinking dazedly when Prissy, resplendent in a new long black veil, caught sight of him and clapped her hands. "Quiet, folks!" she called. "Here's the minister!" She turned to Lee, announcing, "I don't want any remarks here, just a service out of the book at the cemetery. I have a list here of the relatives." She pulled a paper from her dangling black bag. "I'll read the closest relatives first for the front carriages. Abijah Blake!"

When the last relative had scrambled into the carriages, Prissy folded up her list and went too, leaving Lee and the undertaker there alone with the coffin. "Prissy forgot Bill," the undertaker said plaintively in Lee's ear. "I hate to ask it, preacher, but . . . would you mind giving me a hand, hoisting him into the hearse?"

"Fortunately Bill must have been a small man," Lee said to Myrtie later.

"But where did you ride to the cemetery?" Myrtie gasped.

Lee grinned. "With Bill in the hearse, of course!"

The night the Presiding Elder came to hold the first quarterly conference at Townsend since Lee and Myrtie's marriage was the big event of the year for them. No matter how many new members he had added to the church, or how lengthy his list of pastoral calls made, the personal impression a new minister made upon the P.E. was the most important. It was he who, with the bishop, made the appointments, decided who was to get the fat parishes and who the lean and—more important for Lee, who was still a member of the Austin, Texas, Conference—what young men were to be admitted into the New England Conference. It was quite a plum to be asked to join here, for the New England Conference was one of the few which took in only as many ministers as there were pulpits, so that every man was certain of a job.

"They *ought* to ask Lee to join," Myrtie planned fiercely. "They must!" Even if Lee decided to go back to Texas after he graduated from theological school, to be invited to stay here would be a compliment to be treasured. She began to figure ways and means.

She'd cook that P.E. the best supper he ever ate, she decided, for Lee had told her they wouldn't eat until after the Quarterly Conference was over at the church. "I'll make my angel cake, the twelve-egg one that everyone yammers for at the church suppers," Myrtie planned. You couldn't afford to make it very often and it was tricky; you had to practically hold your breath all the time it was in the oven for fear it would fall, but when you finally savored its luscious, frothy goodness. . . .

"This kind comes only by fasting and by prayer," Lee had said reverently when he took his first bite.

But Myrtie was as nervous as a cat on her own hot stove that day the P.E. was coming to supper. When the cake was done, she fried a chicken, worked her fingers rough cleaning wedding silver, and got up on the stepladder to get down the best china with the peacock-blue edge. She could have screamed when Lee came tearing down from the church with the bad news.

"The P.E.'s on a diet!" he gasped anxiously. "He told me to tell you all he wanted for supper tonight was a bowl of bread and milk and some raw fruit."

"Raw fruit!" Myrtie stared at Lee. After getting ready all this! Her back ached and her head ached and she hated the P.E. and didn't mind who knew it. "I've scrimped us for a week to buy all this food and I've worked all day to cook it," she told Lee grimly. "You can go right back and tell that old P.E. that if he isn't hungry, *I* am. He'll eat what we have and like it!"

Lee opened his mouth to answer her hotly, but closed it again, for he'd already learned that, with Myrtie in that mood, silence was prudent. But he looked at her as if he'd nursed a viper in his bosom unaware, turned on his heel, and went back to the church to the Quarterly Conference. After he'd gone, Myrtie flung herself down upon her bed, beat against the wet pillow with her small fists. Lee hadn't known that she'd lost her breakfast the past two mornings. . . .

It was after ten that evening before Lee showed up at the parsonage with the P.E. He was a tall, tired-looking man whose lined face was charming when he smiled. Myrtie with the tears all powdered away with the teensiest bit of flour made even a tired man's eyes light up. She wore her best dress, delphinium blue the color of her eyes, with a lace frill at the neck; she'd washed her hair while the chicken was frying, so that soft little tendrils curled all over her small head. She led the way into the dining room where the table groaned with food. But the P.E. didn't refuse a thing. Lee heaped his plate and Myrtie watched anxiously while he took his first bite. The chicken had been fried in butter the slow Texas way; the biscuits were light as a baby's conscience; and she'd made the ripe tomato conserve herself. The P.E. ate everything right down to the peacock-blue edge and passed his plate back for more. Then Myrtie brought on the vanilla ice cream with maple syrup and Texas pecan sauce—and her twelve-egg angel cake; it stood ten inches high, its golden-brown top oozing sweetness, and so creamy light you couldn't cut it, but had to break it into pieces. The P.E. took his first bite and groaned.

"If I eat all this, I'll likely burst—but it'll be worth it! Young man," he told Lee, "you don't know how lucky you are! I see plenty of brides. I have to eat in six different parsonages every week and some of the food. . . ." He shuddered. "Bullet biscuits, half-raw pig, whipped-cream nightmares. . . . I always take a look at the wife, and when she looks young and flighty, I always tell her my doctor won't let me eat anything but a bowl of bread and milk and some raw—"

Myrtie gasped and the P.E. turned white. "Dear God," he cried reverently, *"did I tell you that?"*

For an instant Myrtie hovered between laughter and tears, and then suddenly Lee whooped and Myrtie giggled and the P.E. joined in. They laughed till their jaws ached and their eyes streamed with tears. When the P.E. was eating his second piece of angel cake, he asked Lee affably, "My boy, how would you and your good wife here like to join the New England Conference? You young people are just the type we're looking for and I think there'll be a few openings next April."

Myrtie didn't wait to hear any more. She left the table hastily and rushed out to the kitchen to do a mad dance in front of the old black stove. You'd done it! Lee's work and your angel cake had turned the trick! Maybe you wouldn't have to get along on ten dollars a week much longer. Tonight you could tell Lee that by next fall there'd be three of you and he wouldn't have to worry, because he'd have not just a supply pulpit, but maybe have a church of his very own. Would you join the New England Conference, good woman? Would you? Myrtie spread her delphinium blue skirts in a deep happy curtsy to the old black iron stove.

Next April, 1895, Lee was ordained deacon and transferred to the New England Conference; and that October young Susie— I—was born.

There was great discussion over what to name the new baby and the first grandchild for the Rouse family. Myrtie was proud of the fact that *her* family was descended from General Richard Montgomery of Revolutionary fame; but it was Lee investigating at the town library who discovered the fly in that ancestral ointment.

"I wouldn't insist upon the general," he chuckled to Myrtie. "You see, he never married. So that would make his descendants bas—"

"Lee Nies!" Myrtie interrupted, pounding, furious, upon his big arm. "*Of course* we're descended from his sister Susan, who *did* marry! *Her* daughter was *Elvira* and *her* daughter, *Susan.* . . . The two names have alternated for generations. My mother is Susan and I'm *Myrtle Elvira,* so if the baby's a girl, naturally she'll be *Susan.* And if it's a boy," she flung her arms around Lee's neck, "shall we name him for General Richard Montgomery? Or for you, you slanderer!"

There was no money to buy baby furniture, so Lee made a bassinet out of an old prune box which he begged at the grocery store and covered with an economical coat of light-blue paint; but Myrtie decked out the prune box with a ruffle of lovely pink silk. When Lee came home and found what she'd done, he was angry for the first time since they'd been married; he'd worried himself almost sick over how they were going to pay the doctor —and here was Myrtie buying yards of expensive pink silk! "I don't *care!*" she flared back. "My baby's going to see something pretty, not CALIFORNIA PRUNES peeking through the paint!"

Susan Rouse sent the baby a lavish layette of lacy, long dresses and soft wool blankets, but there was no high chair or play pen. They'd just have to wait to get a carriage till he got a raise in salary; besides, as Lee pointed out, the baby wasn't even here yet. But Myrtie wanted everything ready; she made Lee put the pink-covered prune box on a chair between the wall and their great walnut bed with its high headboard where the carved grapes hung, heavy, heavy over their heads, so the baby would be near them and couldn't fall out.

The night the baby was born, Lee was sure that Myrtie was going to die. As he tramped up and down the little front veranda hearing her occasional cries when the pains got bad and the doctor ordering, "Now take hold of that sheet and pull, hard!" the sweat broke out on Lee's own forehead. He tried to tell himself, "The Lord giveth and the Lord taketh away," as a minister should; but instead his whole being cried out, "Myrtie, Myrtie! I don't care if we never have a baby. *All I want is you!*"

"Mr. Nies, get out of here," the doctor's voice ordered behind him. "Go take a walk. You're making your wife nervous, tramping this way."

Lee never knew where he went; but when he came back through the moonlit cemetery with its white stones marching rank on rank, oblivious to both birth and death, the little parsonage veranda was full of furniture. He stared for a startled moment, then flung open the front door and ran up to Myrtie's quiet room. She was asleep but she opened her eyes drowsily as Lee came in and dropped upon his knees beside the bed.

"Oh, my darling," Lee gasped. "Are you all right?"

"Of course," Myrtie told him. "And so is Grace Susan."

He looked blankly at the prune box, which held a pink blanket with a head and two small hands sticking out. "She's kind of red," he said doubtfully. "But I guess she's all right. You mind that she's a girl?"

"She's lovely!" Myrtie cried. "I didn't want General Richard Montgomery, anyway!" She looked at Lee and giggled, "I mean, Leopold Adolf would be an awful big name for such a little baby. Look, Lee, her hand's so tiny I can put my wedding ring over it!"

Lee looked at the gold wedding ring making a bracelet for his small daughter, binding the three of them together in a family; he put his cheek against his Myrtie's soft one, hungrily. "You know what's down on our back porch for that little shrimp?" he chuckled. He counted on his fingers, "Two wooden cribs. Four high chairs. A gocart and a big baby carriage. Oh yes, and an old covered cradle I bet is all of two hundred years old! The parish must have left them there, without a word. They're very precious, Johnny's high chair and Mary's little crib, for the minister's baby. . . . I'm glad we're not rich, sugar. We never could have bought her so much love from so many people!"

CHAPTER 5

And Gently Lead

THIS SHOULD HAVE BEEN the summer of Lee's content. He had his young bride, his first child, and the job he wanted most; but suddenly the iridescent soap bubble of his happiness exploded wetly about his ears. During his examinations at theological school that spring, when he was writing his final in the Hebrew Old Testament, Lee's mind went blank. He couldn't remember a word of all he had learned!

The doctor to whom the school authorities sent Lee was grave. "You've been working for fifteen years, since you were nine, without any vacation!" he snorted. "What do you think a man is made of—brass? You must stop work at once, Mr. Nies. Rest. Don't worry. Or I won't answer for the consequences."

Sweat broke out all over Lee's tall, skinny body. "But how can I stop preaching?" he demanded, panicky. "I haven't a cent in the bank, and I have a wife and baby to support!"

The doctor was a sensible man. "Well, take a vacation at home then," he advised. "You mustn't go back to school for at least a year. Do things you wouldn't ordinarily do; things that are fun rather than what you think you ought to do. Take a long walk every day until you're tired enough to sleep. Above all, don't worry."

That made a lot of sense, Lee thought bitterly as he chugged back
to Townsend on the fussy little train. Losing his health was one
hazard to which he had never given an instant's thought, and the
realization that here was something beyond his control that might
stop him at the very moment when he had just entered the New
England Conference, when the tremendous possibilities of preaching were just opening up to him, terrified him. *What if everything
went blank again next Sunday morning so you couldn't remember
your sermon? What were you going to tell Myrtie? You certainly
had made a nice mess of things!* Every turn of the bumpy wheels
that were taking him home to confess defeat said over and over in
his sick mind, "*No good, no good, no good. . . .*"

But all Myrtie said was, "But, darling, it'll be wonderful having
you home! You won't have to go to Boston again for ages." Then
she said the one thing that would drag back a preacher from the
very gates of hell. "Aunt Betsey Fessenden thought your sermon
last Sunday was wonderful!"

Lee's face brightened at once, for in addition to Aunt Betsey's
being his one really wealthy parishioner, he deeply valued her
opinion. Encouraged, Myrtie rushed on eagerly, "She sent us her
tickets for the Boston Symphony for tomorrow night. She'll keep
Susie for us, too, so we won't have to pay a baby-sitter."

"But we can't afford even the train fare," Lee jittered. "We
mustn't spend an extra penny till we see what happens."

"It's medicine," Myrtie insisted. "You still have your student's
ticket and it'll be only fifty cents for me. They're going to play
Handel. Oh Lee, remember the night in Texas when we got engaged? Oh, darling, I want to go!"

They went, of course. But the music did not lift Lee out of
himself as Myrtie had desperately hoped it would. It was the first
time either of them had heard a superlative orchestra, and as the
majestic harmonies sang and thundered about them, Lee found
in them not release, but a world of sound almost too grand to bear.
Beauty can wound as well as exalt when you are deep in the valley
of fear. The climax of the program was Handel's famous *Largo*
and as Lee listened, he trembled all over and tears rolled down his
cheeks. Frightened, Myrtie slid her small warm hand into his and

squeezed frantically; but for the first time since they were married, he did not respond. Her hand slid unwanted from his limp fingers.

"We won't hear music like that again till we stand before the Great White Throne," Lee told her somberly on the way out. "On one side will stand the cherubim and seraphim and thousands upon thousands who have washed their robes and made them white in the blood of the Lamb, chanting, 'Holy, Holy, Holy.' And on the other side will be failures like me. And the end of the world shall come in death and destruction. . . ."

"Yes, dear," Myrtie agreed through cold lips. "Button up your coat, Lee. The night air is chilly." Looking at his still, white face, she wondered, shivering, Is Lee going to die? Is—is he going crazy? She was really terrified that night when he knelt beside their bed to say goodnight to his Lord and Friend as usual. Suddenly he looked up at Myrtie, his face a mask of horror, as he gripped the red and white quilt upon their bed and cried, *"I can't pray! There isn't anybody there!"*

For an instant her heart stopped beating, and then her love for him which was greater than her hope of heaven—or was it a part of all celestial things?—taught her how to comfort him. She held out her warm, young arms and told him, "But *I'm* here, sweet." He went into her arms and lay there more like her son than her husband, till nearly dawn.

It was a terrible summer. Lee kept torturing himself, wondering to Myrtie if maybe he shouldn't resign from the ministry and go back to grinding spices in Texas. A minister who couldn't pray! Oh, he said all the right words in the pulpit on Sunday mornings, but they were a sham; they got no higher than the white-painted ceiling. Every little thing that went wrong in the parish, he was sure was due to his inadequacy. "Have I really made any impression at all on these granite-faced New Englanders?" he agonized to Myrtie. "What have I to offer them but husks?"

She got him to promise that at least he wouldn't resign until fall; he would give himself that long to think things over. Lee stopped giving extemporaneous prayers in the pulpit and instead read other men's prayers; and after service he would go into his study and shut the door and Myrtie would hear him pacing up and down, up and down. Once she almost released him from his promise not to resign yet, when she heard through his closed door the broken cry, "Oh my God, why hast Thou forsaken me?" But Myrtie knew that the Lord hadn't forsaken her Lee; only, for a little while, through no fault of his own but because of his sickness, Lee had lost contact with the Almighty. So she gritted her teeth and held on and waited.

One June morning, in desperation, Lee decided to take the doctor's advice to go for a long walk to tire himself physically as well as mentally. He'd always wanted to follow up the riverbank to find out where the stream began, so he started out. The Squanicook River bustles through Townsend, then wanders off through the fields and woods so quietly that the bending reeds can see themselves in the brown, shallow water. Lee followed the river up till finally the bushes got so thick that he had to turn off across a field that sloped up to a small weathered gray farmhouse he had never seen before. Magnificent by the open doorway was the largest sweetbrier bush he had ever seen, in full bloom, ablaze with pink blossoms where the bees and butterflies were rioting, mad with honey and lush summer.

"What you doin', trespassin' on my land?" a man's voice snarled.

The old man who'd come around the corner of the house wore a ragged blue uniform coat over his heavy bent shoulders; the buttons were half off the coat and the gold braid on the officer's cap pushed back on his iron-gray hair was tarnished black. To complete this fantastic outfit, he wore overalls with one strap gone.

"I lost my way," Lee explained. "I was just admiring your wonderful rosebush. It's the most gorgeous one I ever saw."

"You're either a liar or a fool," the old man told him. " 'Tain't nuthin' but an ole brier." He added several salty cuss words, so that Lee asked, smiling for the first time in weeks, "What're you doing, captain, so far inland?"

Lee's words seemed to please the old man. He swelled out his chest in the spotted, tattered coat, admitting, "I was master of the *Spittin' Susy*, out'a Gloucester, before I sold out, like a dumb fool. When I first made snug harbor, I lived there with my daughter till she like to drove me crazy, yappin' 'Pa, do this!' or 'Don't you dare spit in my flowerpot, Pa!' So I up and married me my old woman and we come up here to get some peace. But it looks like we ain't gonna get much, people bustin' in. . . . Who in hell are you?"

"I'm the Methodist minister up town."

The old captain actually blushed, not knowing how much juicier language Lee had heard as a boy in Texas. "I ain't religious," he mumbled unnecessarily, "but my wife is. She don't get to church none—but I guess you wouldn't want to call on a Hard-Shell Baptist?"

"If she'll put up with a soft-shell Methodist," Lee said.

"Come on, then. She's down washing at the brook."

The old captain led the way back of the house and down through the meadow, and as they waded through the sweet fern and blueberry bushes they could hear the woman singing, "Oh happy day that fixed my choice. . . ." She was a little sprig of a woman, dressed in a long gray calico wrapper, bending over to slosh a blue shirt up and down in the brook; and as they came up Lee noticed, puzzled, that she had a rope around her waist, with the other end tied to a big pine tree. Suddenly she heard them coming, turned, and Lee's heart gave a turn. Why, the old woman was blind!

"Listen, Cap!" When she held up her hand peremptorily for silence, you could hear the birds singing like mad and the brook plucking at its stone harp. She said happily, "Those thrushes are better'n any choir, ain't they? 'N the brook's the organ. But sometimes I get kind of hungry for a real preacher. . . ."

"I brought you one, Angie," the captain told her. "Picked him right out'a our brier bush. This is the Methodist minister, Mr.—"

"Nies," Lee supplied hastily, adding to his own surprise as the sweet-faced old woman beamed at him, "But you may call me Lee, if you like."

"You married, young man—Lee?" she asked.

How had she known you were young? "Yes, but my wife doesn't get around the parish much, now we have the baby," he told her. "It means hiring a horse and carriage."

"And that costs money," she understood, adding wistfully, "but I haven't heard a woman's voice since I married my old man and came here with him to keep house. Maybe someday you can bring your wife up?" She began to pull on her rope, feeling her way across the meadow. "I'll go right up and make us a cup of tea."

Her name was Miz' Angie Summers and the old man was Cap Summers, and in his mind Lee named the place "Sweetbrier Farm." She moved about the familiar kitchen as surely as if she could see, putting a stick of wood in the stove, putting on the kettle, taking the thin company china out of the cupboard with hands that trembled with excitement. Lee watched her, fascinated, deciding that if any visitors had stopped at this out-of-the-way farm, likely the old man had driven them off. They had tea and home-made sugar cookies, and when he left Lee promised to bring Myrtie and the baby to call. He suggested to the captain, "Why don't you bring your wife down to church some Sunday, so she can meet the other ladies? I'll be looking for you both."

But the old captain and his blind wife never came to church. Lee kept his promise to take Myrtie and Susie up to the farm, but the road was so bad that they broke a spring in the buggy and it cost so much to replace that Lee didn't try going again. Weeks went by, months, and Lee forgot all about Sweetbrier Farm except once when he saw another brier bush and noted how all the lovely blossoms were gone, leaving only hard little red apples—and thorns. Under ordinary conditions Lee would have ridden up there again on his bicycle, but this summer he was too taken up with his own black worries as to whether or not he would stay in the ministry to consider even blind, old, lonely ladies.

But just after daybreak one fall morning there came a loud banging on the parsonage door that woke the baby, who began to cry. Lee, stumbling sleepily down in his bathrobe to discover what was the matter, found the old captain standing there on the front stoop. He looked even more disreputable than when Lee had seen him last, for the buttons were all off his uniform coat and his overalls were held together in front with a safety pin; but his face looked more ravaged than his clothes. Something must be terribly wrong at Sweetbrier Farm.

"Is your wife sick?" Lee asked, now wide awake.

The old man began to babble such foolishness that at first Lee thought he was drunk. "I told her you wouldn't come. I warned her!" he mumbled. "I told my old woman that you'd never bless her bastard. But she made me come anyway."

What on earth was he jittering about? Lee wondered. Certainly at seventy-odd his wife wasn't apt to have a baby, legitimate or otherwise; but obviously she needed help or she'd never have sent her old man here to the parsonage at dawn. "Just wait till I dress. Come in, have a cup of coffee, and then I'll go back with you," Lee promised.

But the captain refused to come inside; he waited, shivering, on the little stoop while Lee dressed. He didn't stop for breakfast either but climbed up beside the old man onto the rickety seat of the wagon, hoping it would hold together till they got there. As they rattled along, Lee tried to find out what was wrong at the lonely farm, but the captain just set his lips stubbornly, hunched his shoulders, and spat out over the wagon wheel. As they careened into the farmyard Lee saw something that confirmed his fear of disaster. *There was a light in the front parlor window.* Here in the country, front parlors were opened only for weddings or funerals. . . .

"I knew you'd come, Lee! I knew it!" Old blind Angie's hysterical cry came from the usually tightly locked front door of the house, Lee noted, but the captain was going around toward the back, not even speaking to his wife. What made Angie and her captain act so queerly? When you were here before you'd have sworn that these two old people were fond of each other, but now the look they exchanged over your shoulder was full of—could it be hate?

"Come into the front parlor, Lee," Angie urged, pulling him by the hand. The kerosene lamp was still burning on the marble-topped center table, but the rising sun had made it unnecessary, laying bright fingers of light upon the fair hair of a girl who was asleep upon the narrow horsehair sofa, under the red and green knitted afghan. She lay very still. Lee came closer, then caught his breath sharply as Angie lifted the afghan and the girl's hand slid down limply to the flowered carpet. *She isn't asleep. She's dead!* Lee realized, coldness trickling down his own spine. Tucked in beside her, safe against the sofa back, was a tiny waxen baby, wrapped in a cashmere shawl. Lee touched the small, cold hand, incredulously. *The baby's dead too!*

"This is my niece Marilyn, and her baby," the blind woman introduced Lee gravely as if they were alive. "She was engaged to a man in a factory in Gloucester where she worked—at least she thought she was engaged. She didn't know he was married till a few weeks ago." Angie listened for Lee to say something, but he was far beyond words; he could only stare speechless at the young madonna on the couch and then up at the stern Yankee portraits scowling grimly down at her from the wall. The room was the very pattern of respectability, tidies on the chair backs, big family Bible on the table, pink sea shells and cherished china monstrosities upon the mantel. And in the midst of all this, this girl and her dead baby, alien and yet dominating everything.

"Her mother, my sister, is dead, so Marilyn had no one to come to but me," the blind woman rushed on, stroking back the girl's soft hair from her forehead. Angie gave you the queer feeling that life and death were the same, to her who looked inward instead of outward. The blind woman went on grimly, "She walked the two miles here from the station last night with her birth pains already on her—and then Cap, my old man, wouldn't let her come in!"

"Oh no," Lee gasped. "He wouldn't. . . ."

"Cap told her to go on out to the barn with the other animals," Angie interrupted inexorably. "But I told him, 'If you throw her out, I go too! You're welcome, Marilyn,' I told her. And she came in. Cap didn't want to help me take care of her but I made him. I told him, 'You ain't any angel neither!'"

She hurled the words through the open parlor door so that the old captain heard her, all right. You could hear his heavy feet shuffling uneasily in the kitchen. "We're none of us angels," Lee said slowly. It was only a few years ago that these rock-ribbed Puritans had stopped branding an adulteress with an "A," Lee remembered, trying to be fair; their pride in family integrity was often the only wealth they had, unyieldingly Old Testament. "If thy hand offend thee, cut it off." But how, in God's name, could he. . . .

"I sent my old man for the doctor," Angie related, "but both Marilyn and the baby were—gone—before he got here." There was terrible condemnation in her voice, as if she blamed Cap's delay for their dying and as if the thought of him as a murderer would lie like a sharp sword between them from now on.

Lee drew a deep breath. "But he went for the doctor and he came for me," he reminded Angie gently. "He loved you enough to do that, even against his conscience."

He loved her enough to do that. You could see the realization sinking in, and all at once the bitterness with which she had been bracing herself gave way and she swayed. Lee caught her in his strong young arms and Angie Summers wept bitterly against his shoulder till there were no more tears left. Finally she drew herself away, putting trembling fingers up to smooth her thin hair. She said hesitantly, "I know I got no right to ask it but—would you be willing to say a few words tomorrow over Marilyn and her baby?"

Lee patted her shoulder. "We'll have the finest funeral service for them that this town ever saw. I'll bring the choir from my church, and flowers," he promised recklessly. "Don't you fret. Just leave everything to me."

When Lee started for home, Angie Summers was smiling and pulling up the bright red and green afghan over those two lying there on the couch, as if now maybe she could keep them from being cold.

It wasn't until Lee got back home, and told Myrtie about it, that he realized what a monstrous thing he had promised. Myrtie, gloriously alive in a pink-gingham dress, was laughing at the baby dribbling orange juice down her chin, when Lee burst into the kitchen and explained what had happened. Myrtie went white.

"But, Lee, what if the choir won't go?" she worried. "You remember that girl who had the sailor's 'love baby' last year? They wouldn't even let her be buried in the cemetery! And Angie isn't even a Methodist! She's never been inside our church. . . ."

Oh, darling, if they let your old blind lady down, I can't bear it!"

"It will be a test of my ministry," Lee interrupted her grimly. "If, after listening to me preach all year, they won't help me make this funeral a thing of beauty, my ministry is a failure. We'd best pack right up and go back to Texas. And that's that."

Myrtie stared at him. He meant it; and in a way you couldn't blame him.

"Warmhearted Texans I could have answered for," Lee went on slowly, "but these granite-faced New Englanders like the captain cling to their Puritan taboos harder than any African to his voodoo. Well, I'll give them a chance, anyway." One thing was certain: you couldn't force them to go to the funeral service; they'd go if it was their own free will—or not at all.

"But, darling, you can't change a—a civilization overnight," Myrtie objected, but he acted as if he didn't hear her. It was frightening to see him so grim and tense; there was a lot more at stake than just a funeral. But this was something Lee would have to fight out alone; she couldn't do a thing to help him.

Lee got on his bike and called on as many of the choir and parish as he could manage that very afternoon, but none of them would commit themselves. "Oh?" they said. "You mean down at that lonesome farm?" Or "Hmm, I see." He came home completely baffled. The only ones he was sure would be there were the undertaker and himself.

Lee didn't sleep all night, and an hour before the service the next afternoon he started for the farmhouse. Myrtie parked Susie with a neighbor, borrowed a bike, and rode with Lee; she was afraid not to. She stayed out in the farm kitchen with the old woman while Lee took to pacing up and down in front of the parlor window where he could watch the road, to see if anyone was coming. It looked as if no one was. It got to be fifteen minutes before the hour set for the service, ten minutes, five. . . .

What were you going to say to Angie when no one came? Lee wondered. Very soon now you'd have to begin. . . . He buried his face in his hands trying to pray but still no words came. Face it, you'd failed—utterly.

"Lee, Lee!" Myrtie burst into the room crying, "there's a big cloud of dust coming up the road. Oh, darling, it's a wagon! They're coming!"

The whole parish came. Farmers with calloused hands, uncomfortable in their Sunday suits; their wives wearing birds'-nest hats and with their arms full of flowers from their fall gardens, chrysanthemums and asters. Every single singer in the choir was there! Neighbors who had never crossed the threshold before filled the little parlor where Marilyn lay asleep with her baby, and not a single soul let on by so much as the flicker of an eyelash that here was anything unusual. Lee wrung each hand as they came in. Granite exteriors can be useful, he understood at last, when underneath run streams of clear human kindness.

"Dearly beloved," Lee began. No, that was the wedding service; but that was how you felt about them all anyway. *Rejoicing. Your people hadn't failed you after all!* He began again, "I am the resurrection and the life, saith the Lord. . . ." Suddenly and simply he could pray again; but he didn't have to talk very loud, for the Lord was right there.

So the choir sang and Lee prayed and Marilyn and her baby who had loved life so fiercely and had lost it were laid away with the finest funeral that Townsend had ever seen. It was hard to tell who was happier about it all, Angie or her old captain or Lee. When he and Myrtie finally set out for home on their bicycles, they left the two old people together in the kitchen, having a comfortable cup of tea. As their wheels slid along the sun-dappled river road, Lee began to sing aloud his joy.

"He shall lead his flock like a shepherd. . . ."

As his golden voice rang out joyously for the first time in months, Myrtie's own throat tightened so with thankfulness that she could hardly sing. For the nightmare was over; they would stay. Lee had found his peace again and his Lord. She lifted her chin bravely and joined in.

". . . and gently lead those that are with young. . . ."

CHAPTER 6

The Miracle

LEE BELIEVED IN MIRACLES—or rather, he didn't believe in them at all; he thought they were as natural as rain and sun. "Take making bread out of stone—what's so unusual about that?" he asked Myrtie. "Don't farmers stick seeds into the ground every spring and expect to get grain? What is earth but pulverized stone? The grain is ground into flour which later comes from the grocer's, a miracle wrapped in waxed paper."

"But, Lee, what would happen if someone forgot to put in the yeast?" Myrtie ventured.

Lee threw up his hands. "Of course people can hinder miracles as well as help them along. But the Lord is not limited, because he made all the laws, those we understand and those we don't. The universe goes right on, century after century, never changing; *but our knowledge of it changes*. Scientists are discovering new 'miracles' all the time, but they're new only to *us*. . . ."

"I still think someone has to scratch the ground and knead the dough," Myrtie insisted stubbornly. As Lee escaped toward his study, she raised her voice, "And you needn't slam your study door at me, Lee Nies. I've just as much right to my opinion as you have! What's more, it'll be a miracle if we eat for the rest of this

69

week. I've only got fifty cents in my purse and the milkman won't leave any milk for Susie unless I pay cash. He doesn't know me like they did in Townsend."

Lee had been ordained deacon and transferred from the Austin to the New England Conference in 1895. But since he had taken a year out during his sickness he did not get his degree as Bachelor of Sacred Theology at Boston University till 1897—the same spring the Presiding Elder had written to him about moving to Orient Heights. Myrtie hadn't wanted at all to leave Townsend; she had been appalled when Lee had read the letter aloud to her.

"Don't let the salary listed in the Conference Year Book kid you, Lee," the P.E. had warned, "because you won't get it—not at first, anyway. Orient Heights is in a very tough spot. Not only is the church divided—one faction asked the minister to leave— but their only wealthy contributor walked out in a huff. After his five dollars a week stopped, the minister hardly got enough to eat. But it's a real challenge to a man to get that church going. And you'd never have to go hungry. Just push my doorbell and anything I have is yours."

"He means that," Lee told Myrtie proudly.

Lee *wanted* to go to this divided, unhappy church! Myrtie realized, dismayed. He was like the battle horse in the Bible who "saith among the trumpets, Ha, ha, and he smelleth the battle afar off. . . ."

As her silence got through to him finally, Lee laid down the letter to take his small wife in his arms. "A minister's like a doctor, sugar. People don't really need him till they're sick. You don't mind going, do you?"

Leave the little blue-hazed hills of Townsend they had wandered over during their honeymoon? The house where their child had been born? All the people who were now their intimate friends? She drew a deep, shaking breath. "If you want to go, Lee, that's fine." But she couldn't help asking wistfully, "Do you know what the parsonage at Orient Heights is like?"

The parsonage was a four-room horror, a rented second-floor tenement so dingy that even Lee's books, my crib and high chair, and my two-hundred-year-old cradle which Myrtie now used for a bookcase could not make it seem homelike. I was nearly three now, old enough to like to listen to what the grownups said and try to make sense out of it. As I rushed about investigating the new parsonage, I could hear Myrtie saying ruefully, as she and Lee scrubbed down walls and attacked fly-specked windows, "Don't sit in that chair, Lee! It's got a broken leg. I suppose if I take down that ghastly 'yard of pansies,' the first Ladies' Aider who calls will be the one who donated it. Susie, don't jump on the yellow davenport. . . . Oh *no!*"

For as I bounced up and down, a fluttering cloud of live creatures rose about my startled head. "Moths!" Myrtie wailed.

"We'll haul it right downstairs to the back yard and douse it with kerosene," Lee comforted. "Take the other end, will you? That'll fix it."

It also nearly fixed us. The sofa stank to high heaven for weeks, so that we had to leave the windows open to breathe. But the thing that really worried Myrtie was not having to scrub all the floors with disinfectant before she would allow me to play there, but listening to the man in the downstairs tenement cough and cough, day and night

"You think he's got anything catching?" Myrtie asked Lee anxiously. She glanced at me, sitting in my high chair in smeared pink rompers, feeding Punk cereal. Punk, limp and almost completely hairless from many washings and much loving, was my beloved Teddy bear, without whom I never went anywhere, not even to the bathroom. "I don't dare let Susie play in the back yard for fear she'll put t.b. germs in her mouth!"

"Do you both good to take a long walk every day," Lee said comfortably. "But don't push her uphill in that old carriage. She's getting too big and heavy for you." He smiled at Myrtie. "Especially right now."

What did he mean, I wondered, "especially right now"?

"Who's going to cook, wash, and clean this place when I'm out walking?" Myrtie grumbled. "I have to be here when the milkman comes, to give him cash. He says he don't blame the last parson none for going off owing him a bill, because how could he pay if *he* wasn't paid? But this time he ain't taking no chances. No cash, no milk. After all, he's got kids of his own. . . ." Myrtie stopped quoting as Lee, after searching all his pockets, dropped a crumpled dollar bill into her hand.

"Here," he said triumphantly. "But Mr. Perkins says there won't be any more till next Sunday's collection." Mr. Perkins was the church treasurer. "He's a funny cuss." Lee began to laugh, and his eyes grew very bright and his fair hair stood up in little tufts so that Myrtie wanted to smooth it with her hand. "Brother Perkins hates Mr. Bates so, he never calls him by name—only 'he'. '*He* used to put five dollars in the collection plate every Sunday,' Perkins told me, "but it wasn't any good to the Lord because the money was ground out of the faces of the poor.' "

"It'd be a lot of good to me," Myrtie said practically. "What did Mr. Bates and Mr. Perkins quarrel about?"

"About the union," Lee explained. "Mr. Perkins is a union official and Mr. Bates owns the wool factory, and which one is right about what I don't pretend to know. I'm going up to call on Mr. Bates this morning. I hear he's home with a cold."

Myrtie watched out the window as Lee climbed up the steep hill to the Bates home. You couldn't help seeing it because it was the biggest house anywhere around, built like a stone castle on the top of the hill and staring out toward the faraway blue of Boston Harbor. The big stone house looked like the ogre's castle in the fairy tale, Myrtie thought dreamily, and Lee, getting smaller and smaller, like Jack climbing the beanstalk. She could just see him go through the gate, up to the front door. Why didn't he go in? He was coming back down the hill, very fast.

"The maid said he wasn't in." Lee's mouth twisted wryly. "But I heard him say, 'I've had enough of damn-fool ministers telling me how to run my business. Tell him to get the hell out'a here!' "

"Hell out'a here," I repeated, pleased, from the bedroom where Punk and I were supposed to be taking a nap, but fortunately my parents were too upset to hear me.

"But, Lee, what're we going to do?" Myrtie wailed. "The grocery man makes me pay cash too, because the last minister didn't pay there either. All we have in the house right this moment is oatmeal and a couple of oranges for Susie."

"Don't fuss so, sugar. Let the Lord worry, not you. Don't forget this is His job, too," Lee advised, comfortably. "How about a little kiss for your old man before I go out calling?"

What did you do about a man who refused to worry? Myrtie wondered with his kiss warm upon her lips, as Lee ran blithely down the stairs to call on the parishioners in the neighborhood because he didn't have ten cents to spare for carfare. Did Lee actually expect a miracle to feed them? Was it Elijah or Elisha the ravens fed? No matter. You hadn't noticed any ravens around East Boston, just dirty sparrows fighting in the gutter. Very well, you wouldn't worry. You'd spend your last crumpled dollar for supper. You bet you knew exactly what the horrible Bates man looked like, a fat, red-faced man with a little potbelly. At least Lee always gave you his last penny cheerfully, which was more than some wives could say. That is, he gave it to you if someone who needed it worse didn't meet him first. Myrtie sighed, dressed herself and me, and went out to do some close arithmetic at the corner grocery.

That night my parents' arguing woke me up. The door between their room and mine was always open a crack, so I heard Myrtie say, "If it's a boy, we'll call him Lee. How soon do you think we should tell Susie she's going to have a new brother?" Brother, hunh? I wasn't sure whether I wanted one or not; but one thing was sure; he couldn't have Punk. I fumbled in the dark for his soft, familiar ear, put my thumb back into my mouth, and went to sleep.

The next morning Myrtie looked tired and there was a white line about her mouth as she spooned cereal into my little dish with the cat in the bottom that you had to eat everything up to see. "No miracle, no milk," she said grimly. "So now what?"

"There's a little left in this can!" Lee emerged triumphantly from the pantry to pour it into my dish. "Black coffee is better for you, anyway."

"I like cream in my coffee and I'm not going to pretend I don't," Myrtie said, her cheeks very red.

They didn't say very much as they sat opposite each other sipping coffee and eating dry toast, and when the milkman thumped

up our stairs they just let him bang and then go away. As his footsteps went back downstairs the kitchen tingled the way it does
before a thunderstorm. "I think now's the time to go push the
P.E.'s doorbell," Myrtie said firmly. "I saved carfare just in case
the Lord didn't send a miracle."

She got up, took a dime from her flat purse, and handed it to
Lee. When he didn't move or say anything she went on, "I tell
you right now Susie's going to have her milk for lunch—*if I have
to steal it!* I'll give you till one o'clock."

"I suppose it's your condition makes you so unreasonable," Lee
said, getting up so fast the leg of his blue suit flapped at the knee
and Myrtie began to cry.

"Oh, Lee, you've torn your Sunday suit! There's a big hunk out
of the knee. I can't bear it! It's the very end of the limit. . . ."
Lee caught her in his arms. "Never mind, sugar." He kissed her
and rubbed his cheek against her wet one. If they were going to
have fun, I wasn't going to be left out. Holding Punk by one foot,
I slid down from my high chair, poked my head up under Lee's
arm, and there we all four were—Mother, Punk, and I all safe in
the magic circle of my father's big arm.

But Myrtie wasn't laughing as she tried to mend the jagged hole
in Lee's only Sunday pants. He'd gone off reluctantly in his old
tweed suit, whose trousers were so paper-thin he had to keep his
coat on, to borrow money from the P.E. He hated going and
Myrtie knew he did, but she didn't give in. She stood now in front
of the ironing board, turning the pants this way and that, trying
to draw the jagged ends together, but they simply wouldn't meet.
"I should have learned fine darning at college instead of Beethoven,"
she muttered. Then her face lighted. "I know. I'll patch them with
the old pants I put in the Morgan Memorial bag yesterday. I can
cut a square out of the old ones and fasten it to Lee's good pants
with mending tissue."

"Punk's pants need mending," I announced, holding him up,
but for once she didn't pay me any attention.

As she worked, perspiring with anxiety for fear she wouldn't
do a good job and the patch would pop off when Lee knelt down in
the pulpit next Sunday, her mind slid back over the past four years

of living on love, hope, and a parson's salary. She was beginning to suspect that none of the three was sufficient to bring up a family, and pretty soon there would be four of them. At Townsend it hadn't been so bad because, while there had been little cash, they had always had enough to eat. They had their own and the other farmers' garden and canned stuff in winter; and then there had been the pound parties when everyone brought the minister a pound of food and then stayed on to have a party and eat up half of the gifts!

"But you shouldn't have to depend upon handouts," Myrtie thought rebelliously. "Why, some of the laborers Pa hires at home earn more than Lee does here! Living on donations does something to you. It"—she glanced down at the torn pants before her— "tears your self-respect."

She flushed, remembering about Brother Seton's apples. He had the best orchard of Mackintoshes in Townsend, and his wife always brought a bushel of wormy ones to the parsonage after they'd finished picking and selling. But this year they'd been late coming, so one Sunday morning Myrtie said innocently to Brother Seton, "I hear your Macks are wonderful this year. I can hardly wait to taste them." "They ain't no pinker'n your pretty cheeks," Brother Seton murmured. To Myrtie's great astonishment, he leaned closer, taking her hand and squeezing it as he promised, "I'll bring you down some myself, tomorrow morning. And they won't be wormy, either."

Myrtie had seen to it that she was away when Brother Seton arrived with the apples. Lee couldn't understand why she wouldn't eat any of them, but just made them into applesauce as fast as she could. There was no use telling Lee, and having him make a fuss. Why, it might sound as if she'd tried to vamp Brother Seton into giving them the apples! Thank goodness there weren't many contributors like him, the old fool! She cut a patch out of the old pants viciously, laid it on the good pants, and reached for the mending tissue.

"There!" Myrtie gloated, lifting her iron from the mending tissue. "That's done." It was a work of art if she did say so; the edges were covered so neatly you could hardly tell there'd ever been a tear. She slid the pants leg carefully from the ironing board, folded the crease against the other leg—and burst into loud tears. "Oh, no!" she cried in horror. "Oh, no."

When I came rushing in with Punk to see what was the matter, Myrtie was sitting on the kitchen floor, rocking back and forth, sobbing as if she would never stop. I shook her shoulder. "Mommy. Mommy!" But she just cried harder, so I began to howl too, terrified. She reached out then and put her arm around me, gasping, "I cut the patch out of your father's other good pant leg, instead of out of the Morgan Memorial ones! Oh, Susie! I'm so dumb."

As we sat there on the kitchen floor, the clock in the front parlor struck one with a whirring sound and I said forlornly, "I'm hungry!" My mother wiped her eyes and looked at me. "But not dumber than some people I know," she said grimly. "I'm not waiting any longer. I told your father one o'clock and I meant it. I'm going to pass a miracle or two myself."

She got up briskly, led me into my room, and began yanking off my play clothes. "Are we going to walk?" I asked hopefully. "Can Punk go, too?"

"We're going to put on that pretty pink coat and hat your grandma sent you from Texas and the three of us are going to walk right up that hill and vamp that fat old Mr. Bates!" There were two red spots in my mother's cheeks. "If he can turn away a hungry baby. . . ." A queer reckless light came into her eyes as she went on, "I'm going to wear my new blue hat. Your father says it makes my eyes look like rain-washed gentians." She sniffed. "We'll fix that old Mr. Bates!"

It was fun being pushed up the steep hill in my big old carriage, looking back down the hill to the sparkling waters of Boston Harbor so far below us. "Look, Punk, there's a big ship!" Above us the windows of the great stone Bates home sparkled in the sun like so many eyes watching us come. My mother, pushing the heavy carriage up the hill, was breathing hard, but it wasn't only because the hill was so steep and her body heavy. Even I could see she was scared.

"Here, let me help you with that, girl," a man's voice offered behind us. He scolded Myrtie, "That carriage is too heavy for a little thing like you to push up this hill!"

He was a tall handsome man with silver hair who stood as straight as if he were leading a parade. Myrtie looked at me apprehensively as she surrendered the carriage because usually I didn't like anyone to push me but her; I'd probably howl. But even at three, woman are unpredictable. I smiled at the tall man, demanding, "Susie wants a ride on her cow pony!"

Myrtie laughed, explaining, "She likes you. She wants you to carry her. I'm afraid she's spoiled."

The tall man grinned, reached down, and lifted me to his big shoulders, settling one of my pink-clad legs on either side of his handsome head. Punk dangled from one hand and I gripped his hair with the other, and so we rode regally up the hill, with Myrtie smiling at the three of us with her eyes the color of rain-washed gentians. I'll never forget how lovely she looked with her cheeks blazing from the climb, her face soft with laughter, while behind and below her the sky and sea laughed too. She looked like spring when the little leaves begin to come out, so soft and young you can't believe them real. The tall man could hardly take his eyes off her. He introduced himself, "I'm Tom Bates. You live up here on the hill too?"

Myrtie gasped. She stood still, gripping the handles of the carriage so hard her knuckles were white, and stared up at him. The pretty color had gone from her face, but she lifted her brave chin. "I'm Myrtie Nies, the wife of the new Methodist minister—the one you told to go to hell yesterday morning."

As she stood there, pale, waiting for the storm to break, I put in my two cents' worth. "And this is Punk," I introduced the hairless bear by dangling him in front of Mr. Bates's nose. "He's a Methodist too."

Tom Bates threw back his head and shouted with laughter. He laughed so hard that Myrtie had to join in and so did I, especially loud because I hadn't the faintest inkling what was so funny. "I guess the joke's on me. After all, I did pick you two girls up," Tom Bates admitted, wiping his eyes. "This young lady of yours looks exactly like my son Jimmy when he was her age. About

three, isn't she? He was a riot too." We were in front of the big
stone house by now and Tom Bates pushed open the gate, inviting,
"Come in and meet Mrs. Bates, won't you? She'd like to see Susie
and Punk."

The house inside was full of soft oriental rugs scattered on lovely
bare slippery floors where you could slide while the grownups
were busy talking. We were invited to lunch and we stayed—you
can bet we did, with only dry cereal waiting for us at home.
Somehow this fact slipped out, and pretty soon Myrtie was telling
Mrs. Bates the whole story. She was the sort of person you did
tell secrets to, a tiny gentlewoman with gray hair, brown eyes,
and a voice as soft as April rain. I fell asleep at the table with
my head in the tray of their son Jimmy's old high chair that had
been brought down from the attic.

I only half woke as my carriage rolled back down the hill with
Mr. Bates pushing it on his way back to the wool factory from
lunch. As we stopped at our tenement door I heard him say, "Don't
argue. It's settled. That apartment of mine hasn't been rented for
three months; you might as well use it." A cough came out of the
open window of the floor below ours, and he scowled. "That man
downstairs has had t.b. for years. We can't take any chances with
Susie and Punk."

But our day of miracles had just begun. Lee was waiting for us
upstairs with a five-dollar bill! He hadn't gone to the P.E. after
all; just before he got on the street car he'd met Brother Perkins,
who'd been worried about the minister's family and had loaned
Lee a bill. "It's simply raining miracles," Myrtie giggled. "Oh,
Lee, Mr. Bates is *nice*. And his wife's a darling."

As the two of them climbed into the big brass bed that night, Lee
asked Myrtie if she figured she could afford to bake a cake for
tomorrow night. Mr. Perkins and Mr. Bates were going to drop
by to see him.

"Both of them?" Myrtie gasped. "*Together?*" She drew the red
and white crazy quilt the Ladies' Aid had given them last Christmas
up under her chin. Each little piece had the name of a parishioner
written on it in indelible ink and Myrtie had loved it ever since
she'd found, sewed right side by side, the names of two women

who weren't speaking to each other. "I heard you phone Mr. Bates just now to thank him for our lunch—but how will you get Brother Perkins to come too?"

"Oh, I asked him this morning when he gave me the money," Lee explained.

Myrtie stared at him. Dear Lee. He had the faith and you were the works. He counted on a miracle but you had to work for it. Mr. Bates might have asked you in to lunch anyway, but it hadn't done any harm to wear the gentian-blue hat. What was Lee saying about labor and capital being two legs of the same man? She yawned. "Don't preach, darling. I'm your wife; remember me?"

He kissed her, but his heart would not be in it till he got this off his chest, she knew resignedly. "I have an idea," he told her dreamily, "that when the Lord gets ready for the Judgment Day, he won't spend a thousand years adding up our mistakes and subtracting them from our virtues like some celestial bookkeeper. He'll just look over his spectacles and ask, 'My son, would you be happy in heaven?'"

The third miracle took place the next night in Lee's study. Brother Perkins looked as if he'd bitten into a lemon when he saw Mr. Bates sitting there in the big chair already, but Lee didn't give them time to begin fighting. He locked the study door and put the key in his pocket.

"You two don't have to speak to each other, but you're going to talk to God," he told the two scowling men. "I don't care a whit who's right in this argument. But you're both going to act like Christians and church members. Now get down on your knees. Tom Bates, you pray first."

They were so startled, they obeyed. Tom prayed first; then Brother Perkins mumbled a prayer; and finally Lee started the Lord's Prayer, which they all repeated together. "For Thine is the kingdom, the power, and the glory. . . ." These words were too big for any littleness. As they got up from their knees, Tom Bates held out his hand silently and Brother Perkins took it; so Lee knew that the dispute at the wool factory was as good as settled, and the church trouble too. He unlocked the study door and called loudly, "You got anything good to eat, Myrtie?"

We moved into Tom Bates's clean little white apartment the very next week, and the following Sunday he and his wife came back to the church service and put the five dollars into the collection plate, exactly as advertised. Tom didn't always come, but his wife was always there with the precious bill and when Tom did come, he passed the collection plate, along with Brother Perkins. Old members drifted back to see the two enemies walking down the aisle together side by side as ushers; and after they'd heard Lee preach, they stayed on. Myrtie served cocoa and cookies, helped by the Ladies' Aid, every Wednesday night after prayer meeting till the crowd got so big they had to move out of the vestry into the auditorium. It was a healthy sign when you had to push people out of the church to lock up.

We were never hungry again. As Lee explained, "When you get a church to praying together, finances and all the other problems look out for themselves." But it was his young people who were closest to his heart. He took them on picnics, played baseball on empty lots, and had long arguments about the state of the universe in which he sat silent as well as talked. "Kids are worth listening to," he told Myrtie. "They aren't frozen into a mold yet."

Myrtie played the church organ, whose stops were so worn she could never be sure whether the music was going to whisper or roar, and led the young people's choir. How those teen-agers loved to sing! They'd move down from the choir loft in a body to sit in the front seats of the church while Lee threw stereopticon slides of the grand old hymns upon a sheet. What if the boys held hands with their best girls in the dark while they bellowed the hymns? Small wonder the choir grew and grew.

That Christmas Lee planned to have a "White Gifts for the King" pageant when the part of the mortgage they'd been able to pay off would be laid before the altar, and when fifty young people dressed in white would join the church. The local paper wrote a piece about the coming service; and next morning Lee received a telephone call that rocked him back on his heels.

"It's from the pulpit committee of Centenary Church!" he told Myrtie. "The chairman wants me to come to his office on Congress Street tomorrow."

They stared at each other, wide-eyed. Centenary was one of the largest churches in New England Methodism and its pulpit had been vacant for nearly six months because the congregation, who could afford to take their time, couldn't find anyone to please them. "It's got the most gorgeous parsonage," Myrtie breathed. "I went there once to a tea for the bishop. You don't suppose. . . ."

"Of course not!" Lee didn't dare to believe. "They—they might want me to supply a Sunday next summer, maybe."

"I'm going to look up the salary anyway," Myrtie cried, running for the Year Book. She looked up with very blue startled eyes, for the salary was listed at five thousand dollars! At the last meeting of the Ladies' Aid, Myrtie hadn't been able to take off her coat because her blouse had been merely a front tied behind with tape. Since the last of her trousseau went she hadn't bought anything new. She licked dry lips, murmuring, "Susie could have oranges every day! And I'll need so many things for the new baby. . . ."

But this was too much of a miracle for even Lee to count upon.

He was shaking inside as he walked next morning into the imposing gray entrance of the great building on Congress Street, to be shot up eight stories in the elevator. The front office of the chairman of the pulpit committee was as big as the vestry of Lee's church, with armies of secretaries rushing over its thick oriental rugs. They paid small attention to the young man in the shabby blue serge suit until he gave his name timidly.

"Go right in, Mr. Nies," the girl smiled at him. "You're expected."

In a dream from which he never wanted to wake Lee crossed the shining parquet floor to where the chairman sat behind his vast mahogany desk with three telephones. The great man got up and held out his hand graciously. "Sit down, Mr. Nies. We're both busy men so I'll come straight to the point. We visited your church at Orient Heights a month ago to hear you preach—no, we didn't stop to talk to you. The church was mobbed and we slipped out before the benediction. We didn't like to raise false hopes."

The chairman reached for the folded newspaper upon his desk

and slapped it lightly. "That was what decided us. Any preacher who can get fifty young people to join his church is the man for us. *We would like you to be our new pastor at Centenary. How soon can you come?*"

Lee stared at him, hardly able to breathe, let alone speak. It had all happened too fast to take in. So many older, wiser men had angled for that pulpit. He gulped, "Perhaps the bishop won't. . . ."

"Oh, he'll be agreeable." The chairman interrupted impatiently. "A large hunk of his salary comes from Centenary, don't forget. I suppose you know what we pay? We're prepared to raise it from five thousand at the end of the year, if you make good."

"Fine," Lee managed. No more scrimping. Myrtie wouldn't have to cut up one leg to mend the other. Maybe you could even have a new suit. Two new suits, he planned recklessly, one blue serge for calling and a good black one for Sundays, like the P.E. What was the chairman saying?

"It takes a young man to attract other young people. That's why we're prepared to overlook your—er—inexperience in other matters."

His young people. Suddenly instead of the impressive office with its rich, thick rugs and shining mahogany, Lee was seeing the crowd of youngsters pushing by him last Sunday at the door of his shabby church as he stood there, shaking hands. "See you next Sunday, Padre!" one boy had called and Lee had called back, "Sure thing, Bill." But if you went to Centenary, you wouldn't be there when Bill came. Lee got up so abruptly his chair fell over backward.

"I can't come," he told the startled Centenary chairman. "I don't know what I've been thinking about. You see, the church—*my* church—has just began to *toddle*. I've got to be sure it can walk on its own legs before I leave. I'm sorry if I've wasted your time." He started for the door.

"Wait a minute, young man," the older man roared. Did this young upstart in the shiny blue suit think he could turn the Centenary committee down and get away with it? Lee kept on walking. He really meant it, the financier saw angrily. Or was he just playing it smart? He snapped, "Okay, name your own salary. I'll meet the difference out of my own pocket."

"Oh, it isn't that!" Lee assured him hastily. "It's just that my young people need me."

"Nobody is as important as that. They can get someone else."

"So can you," Lee pointed out. "Centenary is well organized, ready to go places. I can't come, but thank you very much for asking me. I'll always remember it. Good-by."

As the door closed upon the outraged bewilderment of the financier's face, Lee knew he'd made a powerful enemy in the New England Conference, and that he'd never be offered Centenary again. But it wasn't until he was rattling home in the street-car to East Boston that doubts began to assail him about telling Myrtie. Should he have consulted with her before he turned down the magnificent salary, especially with the new baby coming? Babies and doctors—Lee shivered and his throat was dry. Would Myrtie understand why he'd had to do it? The closer he got to home, the more unlikely it seemed. He walked three times around the block before he finally got up courage to go in his own front door to face her, where she was waiting for him so eagerly.

She knew at once that something was wrong. The lovely eager light went out of her face as she gasped anxiously, "Oh, Lee, didn't they . . . ?"

"Oh, they offered me Centenary all right. But I didn't take it," Lee blurted out. As she stood there, stunned, he tried to explain but even to himself the words sounded smug, unbelievable. "Those new kids who are joining the church next Sunday. . . . If I leave now, a lot of them will too. They haven't any roots yet. I've got to stay." His eyes begged her silently to understand; if she didn't he didn't see how he could go on.

She tried desperately to pretend it didn't matter. But her lips were white with shock and as her face went plain, he noticed for the first time how heavy and awkward she had become. She was usually so gay you hardly noticed. She cried desperately, "I bet there isn't another man in the Conference can boast he turned down Centenary!" Then she burst into tears, ran to their room, and shut the door. An hour later she came out, her eyes swollen, but her

head high, her lips smiling if her eyes could not. She put on a
brave show, but not quite good enough. Lee could hear the questions shouting silently between them all through supper. "How are
we going to pay the doctor? Buy another crib? Are you expecting
another miracle, Lee, while you throw good jobs away? What
could happen better than Centenary?"

All that week things were different between them; it seemed as
if the delicate antennae with which they used to touch each other,
to understand without words, had shriveled away. Myrtie retreated into the protecting shell of her approaching motherhood
and became no longer a wife. She never once intimated that Lee
had failed her by not thinking first of her and his family, but
she was too carefully gay. Daytimes she buried herself in mountains
of tissue paper, wrapping her inexpensive gifts for the family in
Texas, and nights she was often away, rehearsing the choir for
the special music on Christmas Sunday. Lee could reach out his
hand to touch her across their small gate-leg table at dinner, but
her real self was, for the first time since their marriage, shut away
from him.

A letter came from Fort Worth from Isaac Rouse offering to
pay Myrtie's expenses if she'd come home to Texas to have her
baby.

"Perhaps this time it'll be Isaac Rouse, Jr.!" Myrtie's father wrote
hopefully. He'd wanted a son for thirty years and had only three
daughters. A grandson would be almost as good. "You're going?"
Lee asked Myrtie. She nodded, not meeting his eyes. "What else
can we do?" She didn't add, "Since you can't take care of me and
our baby." But she might as well have, Lee knew miserably.

One night in desperation, trying to shock her into coming back
to him, Lee suggested that perhaps she would prefer his leaving
their big brass bed and sleeping in the guest room. To his horror,
Myrtie agreed. "Probably it'd be more comfortable for you for
the next few weeks." There was nothing at all he could do about
it. He couldn't blame her, and yet how else could he have acted
honestly and have kept his self-respect as a minister of the gospel?
Had not the Lord denied his own family? "But you are certainly
no Messiah," Lee tortured himself.

On Christmas Sunday the church was filled to the last pew with beaming families and friends of the young people, Lee's young people, who were going to join the church. There is a little of the ham actor in every good preacher, so, although such "popery" was frowned upon by many, Lee had borrowed a long black gown to wear for the ceremony of accepting the "White Gifts for the King." The church smelled sweet with the pine twisted about the chancel railing as Lee stood there watching his young people come down the aisle two by two, the girls in their white dresses and the boys with their painfully slicked hair. The prettiest girl, a blonde with enormous brown eyes, carried a great white box tied with snowy ribbons with the check for the mortgage inside. She smiled up at Lee as she offered the gift before the high altar. Money didn't matter, Lee knew; the real gifts for the Lord were their lifted young faces, lovely blank pages still to be written upon with the beauty of service. As they stood there, Lee and his children, Myrtie's organ behind him suddenly burst into Christmas song, and the voices of the robed choir followed, soaring.

"Hallelujah. Hallelujah . . . for the Lord God Omnipotent reigneth. . . ."

It was their song, his and Myrtie's! As he turned to look up at her, her face in the organ mirror was a small fierce sun shining down at him proudly, and he knew that she'd planned this as a message to him, *to tell him that he hadn't failed, that he'd won! Myrtie understood!* As the music rolled, shouting, over his head, Lee's throat contracted and he had to fight back tears of joy. Even when the chorus ended, he couldn't speak at once to pronounce the benediction. For in a blinding flash of understanding, he saw that the real miracle that had happened to him was not winning over Mr. Bates, or the church's growing so fast, or even being offered one of the largest pulpits in New England—*it was the miracle of Myrtie's love.* Knowing this, his tongue was loosened. He lifted his flowing, black-robed arms and promised his waiting people and his dear love, "The Lord be with thee . . . make his face to shine upon thee . . . and give thee peace."

CHAPTER 7

Preacher in Politics

THE NEW BABY born in Fort Worth was a boy, and his name was Isaac Rouse Nies.

Myrtie, drowsy in her bedroom on the morning after he was born, heard her exultant father call from his veranda across the street to his sister-in-law, "Sylvia, Isaac, Jr., is here! He weighs eleven pounds, a real whopper!"

"I wanted to call him Lee but it would have broken Pa's heart to call him anything else," Myrtie reported ruefully to her husband when she got back home with Ike and me. "We'll just have to wait for the next boy."

Ike was a big placid baby with a happy smile and no hair to speak of, far too heavy for Myrtie to lift. At first I ran errands for him eagerly, as proud of him as my parents, but gradually it began to seep through to me that the parishioners who used to fuss over me as the minister's little girl had now transferred their admiration to this toothless, plump creature who did little to earn it but gurgle and burp. It was a bitter moment when I realized I had been deposed. More humiliating, after he was old enough to walk I had to stay as close to the house as Ike did, for fear he would get loose from the rope where Myrtie had tied him to a tree and crawl toward the dangerous pond that was nearby. It was just the sort of thing he would do merely to get attention, I thought savagely. One day I got fed up and presented Ike to the milkman.

"Take him away," I urged. "We don't need him any more."

Amused, the milkman seated the jovial Ike obligingly among his milk bottles and clip-clopped away, thinking the little boy might enjoy a ride. Meanwhile Myrtie came out into the yard, found Ike missing, and was immediately certain he'd been either drowned or kidnaped. Either seemed to me an excellent idea, so I stayed mute during all the excitement while my weeping mother summoned the neighbors, and the police came roaring up to the parsonage in great style. They were just about to dredge the nearby pond when the milkman rattled back with Ike, placidly chewing a bottle top.

The jealous rivalry between Ike and me worried Lee and Myrtie, but they couldn't seem to do much to lessen it. At three Ike was at the pestiferous age. When the rest of us older kids played hide-and-seek in the meadow, Ike would sit in front of where I was crouching and yell, "I see Susie!" He broke my dolls and chewed up a large exercise book where I'd been writing down my cherished "poems." On the other hand, I bossed him unmercifully.

"Maybe if we let Susie do something Ike can't, she'll quit being jealous of him," Lee suggested one night to Myrtie. "Why don't I take her to class meeting with me tonight and you put Ike to bed?"

Ike looked like an angel going to bed in his long white nightgown, but he pinched me as he went by and I let out an anguished yelp. "Get your hat," the long-suffering Lee urged. "Let's go, Susie. Do you realize you'll be staying up *after eight o'clock at night?*"

In those days, class meeting in our church took the place of both the confessional and the psychiatrist's couch, where anyone could get spiritual and emotional catharsis by relating to other avid church members the interesting ways in which he had sinned and repented during the past week. Every Tuesday evening our small vestry was mobbed by seekers for human drama more thrilling even than the neighborhood movie because you knew the actors intimately. This was my first experience of such exciting details as how a man had hit his wife and then "repented in sackcloth and ashes"; another man, a janitor, had found a five-dollar bill and, after a night of soul searching, returned it to the owner. "Amen! Glory be!" shouted thin little Brother Wentworth down in the front seat; it seemed incredible so much noise could come out of so skinny a little man. But I loved this dramatic evening; and swiftly the urge grew in me to be an actor too.

"Would anyone else like to testify?" Lee asked.

With my heart thudding so hard it shook me all over, I slid to my feet. I was just tall enough to see over the chair in front of me, but I piped loudly, "I could be a Christian too, if it wasn't for that awful Isaac Nies!"

I waited for Brother Wentworth to shout "Amen!" but instead a sickening wave of laughter swept over my head. What had I said wrong? I wanted to run far, far away, but waves of horror rooted me to the floor. If Dad laughed too. . . . But when I lifted my eyes to his, they were solemn and very calm. "We all have our Isaacs," Dad said gravely. "You can sit down now, Sister Nies. We will all sing Hymn Number 36."

That was the end of my being jealous of my handsome brother; if my father could treat me as a grown-up contemporary, it behooved me to become one.

Lee's move to Stanton Avenue Church, Dorchester, had been the result of the bishop's insistence. In those days, Methodist ministers were tacitly expected to move every three years, on the theory that in that way they would pick no favorites in the parish, and the church, not the minister who happened to be in charge, would be the more important. For this reason after the Orient Heights Church was able to stand on its own feet, Lee was sent to South Framingham for three years and then shifted to the rising young church in Dorchester, a parish which was growing almost as fast as the community which was being rapidly built up. Lee was to break all rules and records by staying and growing with this church for nine long years; but he wove himself so closely into the life of the whole neighborhood that not only did the

Stanton **Avenue** committee plead with the bishop to let him stay, but even the ward politicians put in their word.

A preacher in politics was an anathema in the early 1900s. Lee didn't want the job; he got into politics by the back door, through trying to build up the S.A.M.E.C. Club in his church vestry where the neighborhood boys could come in off the street to play games and to run around a track, instead of beating up policemen. It was only a second step to try to get rid of the saloons in the same ward, whose brightly lighted bars were the only other clubrooms available. And fighting the saloons soon got Lee into practical politics.

Lee hated saloons. He had seen enough of them in his early days in Texas; he had seen murder committed there; and he did not think they were good clubhouses for teen-agers. But where else in the neighborhood were they welcome? Aimless gangs of them wandered the Dorchester streets every night. Frequently they threw stones through the Stanton Avenue Church windows and often the church notices that Lee had pinned to the bulletin board by the front door had ribald comments scrawled on them in crayon. The situation grew more serious when a gang of boys, angered by the clubbing of one of their members, jumped on the offending policeman and beat him up so badly he was sent to the hospital.

One evening George Doggett, a member of the official board at our church, on his way to a committee meeting, had his hat ripped off by a stone thrown by one of the gang hanging about the lamp post in the very shadow of the church. As he picked up his hat, George asked the boy curiously, "If you had a clubroom—say, in the church over there—would you come? Do you like to play basketball?"

"Do I look like a Sunday-school kid?" the boy scoffed. But one of the other boys yelled, "He was captain of the high-school team before he got a job, mister!"

George dropped a bombshell into the official board meeting that night. "That gang outside are good kids," he insisted earnestly. "If we don't give them something to do, we'll pay board for a lot of them in jail one of these days. I move we invite them to use our vestry as a club nights. We could buy a secondhand pool table, games. . . ."

"They'd wreck the place!" an older member of the committee protested, outraged. "They aren't our boys!"

"They ought to be." Lee came to George's assistance. One of the chief reasons for his success in the ministry was that he did not have to have an idea first to find it good. He promised the committee, "I'll be responsible for replacing anything that gets broken. I move, gentlemen, that George be voted the necessary funds to go ahead at once."

George and Lee worked fast. When the lights flashed on three nights a week in the Stanton Avenue Methodist Episcopal Church vestry, the boys flocked inside to see what this new church joint was like—and stayed to box or play games. In a few weeks the S.A.M.E.C. Club—using the initials of the church as a name—was in business. Soon both lower vestries were pressed into use, one fitted up as a gymnasium where boys could wrestle on the mats or play basketball; the other with easy chairs, games, books, and bright floor lamps. The only admission card was, as one boy put it "You gotta play clean or get out. And no bottles on the hip." Older men were there from the church every night to start the games and keep order, and usually Lee or George Doggett dropped by to encourage "bull sessions" or to referee basketball. But very soon the S.A.M.E.C.'s took over their own disciplining. After they had shown they meant business by ganging up on a couple of belligerent newcomers, no more windows were broken in the church. Lee did have to replace a couple of chairs which were mysteriously shattered, but the father of one of the S.A.M.E.C.'s who brought the new chairs stayed for the evening, and, after watching the boys, refused any pay.

"You know," he marveled, "I think I've come to understand my own kid for the first time."

That spring the S.A.M.E.C.'s baseball team cleaned up in the interchurch league, and that winter their basketball team won the pennant.

Very little was said about church membership, but the Sunday-school class George Doggett led on Sunday mornings drew from thirty to sixty boys; it was something to see these adolescents pouring in, with their hair slicked down as if they were dating girls. The room seemed about to burst with pent-up energy. But the weeknight S.A.M.E.C. sessions included boys of nearly every creed, Protestant, Catholic, Jewish, and from no church at all. Lee was starting a series of Friendly Sunday Evening Services where he turned the ushering and the taking up of the collection over to the S.A.M.E.C's. One Saturday night Lee came to George Doggett, chuckling.

"Who do you think wants to usher at the service tomorrow night? Sammy Vishinski! He said to me, 'I suppose you won't want me because I'm a Jew,' but I told him, 'A Jew started the Christian church, Sammy.'" Lee grinned at George. "But I bet it'll start a rustle when Sammy struts down the aisle tomorrow night with the collection plate!"

Bit by bit Lee's church was becoming a power in the whole community, not just a Sunday visitor. He started a discussion group Sunday mornings for older men, many of them S.A.M.E.C. fathers, to take up the question, "What would Jesus have done in Dorchester?" The group grew so large they had to move up from the vestry to the auditorium and organized themselves into the "Nies Club." It was only a step from talking about them to wanting to do something about their neighborhood problems. "Local option" was then in force in Massachusetts, so that a ward could choose for itself whether or not liquor should be sold within its limits. Watching the S.A.M.E.C.'s thoughtfully, the Nies Club decided too many saloons could become a neighborhood menace. Over a hundred of them rang doorbells, where householders greeted them enthusiastically; and when the vote came in November, the saloons were out in Ward 24.

The very next morning an anonymous letter was put through the slot in Lee's front parsonage door. "Mind your own business. Stay on your side of the tracks (most of the remaining saloons were across the Norfolk Street streetcar tracks) or else." Lee tossed the note in his study wastepaper basket and went on as usual, but the letters continued to come. Finally he showed one to Myrtie which warned, "Look out for your wife, you dirty ward boss!"

"My goodness, don't they know I grew up in Texas?" Myrtie asked, scornfully. "I used to be pretty good with Pa's .44. All I need is a little practice."

Soon thereafter the neighbors were startled to hear the minister and his wife popping away at bottles in their back yard. Ike and I wanted to "shoot, too," so Dad stuck a firecracker in one end of an empty spool and a long pencil in the other end. We achieved a lovely bang. But Myrtie hadn't been boasting; she was as good a shot as Lee. They weren't really worried; but after all, the policeman had been beaten up. Even hostile boys or crackpots could do a lot of damage.

Before the next election the Nies Club invited each candidate for office to come to explain what he stood for and what he meant to do for Ward 24 and their sons. When the men from other clubs in surrounding churches came to listen too, the ward political bosses began to get worried. What if the church vote should really unite, and realize their power? This could be dangerous. A local paper ran an article belittling Lee as a "preacher in politics" who didn't know what he was talking about. What did a Methodist parson know about "the people's clubhouse"? Most objectors to the poor man's saloons were either snobs or hypocrites. Probably Lee Nies had never been inside one. Did the church think it could run the state? The clergy should take care of the next world and let "practical people" manage this.

"Them was fightin' words" to a Texan. Lee preached the follow-ing Sunday on "Am I a Worm or a Soldier of the Cross?" The church was full. Certainly the church in free America had no right to run the state, he agreed, or vice versa.

"But I am profoundly concerned about the Christian duty of Ward 24 citizens," Lee thundered. "I propose to find out each candidate's record, and put him on record publicly. Then I urge you to vote for whomever you like. *But vote!*"

Lee had stepped into the political puddle up to his neck, he discovered soon enough, but the whole Nies Club was in there with him. For the first time the church people had learned what power, united, they might wield; and power is a headier brew than even whisky. They decided to run a candidate of their own for state senator and persuaded a retired Baptist minister named Swett to run, on the dual platform of the separation of church and state and no liquor sold in Ward 24.

Swett didn't expect to win the primary, but the church men began ringing doorbells again. At first the ward bosses were not particularly worried and the newspapers made sly jokes about how Ward 24 was "Swetting it out." To make the nomination of their own man doubly sure, the ward bosses persuaded another pillar of the church to enter the state senatorial race against Swett, hoping thus to split the church vote. On the night before election, the newspaper prognosticators didn't give Swett a prayer to get in. Lee himself was so worried that he spent hours calling in all his workers to a last-minute rally—but only seven men showed up.

"Even the Nies Club is letting me down," Lee told Myrtie, the hurt, weary lines deepening about his mouth.

Next morning the newspaper headlines screamed, BAPTIST MINISTER WINS EVERY PRECINCT IN WARD 24. When the bewildered, jubilant Lee asked his workers why they had not attended the rally the previous night, they explained "But everyone had already decided how to vote!"

Two days later an enormous red Mercedes drew to a stop in front of our modest white parsonage where Ike and I were playing jackstraws on the top step. We gaped, goggle-eyed, at the well-dressed, pompous man with the white carnation in his buttonhole, for whom the chauffeur was holding open the door. The pompous one asked, "Little girl, is this the residence of the Reverend Nies?"

"Yup," I agreed, one of my long black stockings falling down as usual when I got up to usher him into our house. I looked up at him doubtfully, but, being given to drama, I could not resist the temptation. I urged, "Come in, poor dying sinner, and he'll pray for you!"

Probably a politician never had a more astounding welcome, for he was still standing there, startled, in our front parlor when Lee came running down the stairs. As a worker for the United States senator from Massachusetts the politician had met many hazards in his career, but he had never been prayed for of a Thursday morning! He drew himself together, however, explaining to Lee that he had come to ask his support for Senator Henry Cabot

Lodge in the coming election. This famous senator, the friend of kings, sending an emissary to a young Methodist minister! Lee would have been less than human not to feel flattered. Still, why not? Was it not the essence of a democracy to admit that however tall a man might grow, his roots were still deep in the earth of our common origin? It was this very brotherhood which had brought Lee's own father to this country.

"What do you want, Nies?" the other man asked without further preamble, for after all, this young parson was pretty small potatoes, politically speaking. If the senator hadn't been having trouble with his constituency because of his isolationist sound-offs in Washington, he wouldn't have needed the Dorchester church votes; but as it was. . . . The politician assured Lee, "We'll promise you anything within reason for delivering the solid church vote in this ward, but we won't be held up, see? Oh I don't mean money. I mean—"

"I know what you mean." Lee's face was a fiery, humiliated mask. This man meant power for power; patronage for votes. His only interest in the church was to nail it as a slat to the senator's political fence. This man in the big red Mercedes wasn't a big man at all, merely a sounding brass and a tinkling cymbal—a "practical politician." To him the American credo "of the people, by the people, for the people" was a moth-eaten flag to grab out of his bag of tricks, to wave on the Fourth of July or just before election day.

"Well?" the politician snapped, uneasy in the continued silence; and Lee, looking deep into his eyes, saw something that tempered his own anger with pity. *The other man's eyes were afraid.*

"There's nothing *you* can give *me*," Lee told him gently. "But if the senator wants to come to our 'Good Citizen Night' to talk to our church men, he will be welcome—like any other candidate."

That is how Governor Draper of the sovereign state of Massachusetts and United States Senator Henry Cabot Lodge came out to Lee's little brown church in the hinterlands on September 26, 1910, to eat chicken and cole slaw (or so it reports on the yellowed menu) with 562 Nies Club men and their guests from nearby churches. The Ladies' Aid outdid themselves with the supper, and Lee reflected dryly that at least the Nies Club had made a United States senator come to them.

Senator Lodge was reelected but Swett, the Ward 24 candidate, was defeated for senator in the state elections. Lee and his men began immediately to look for another man who might win next year. Both political parties now sent emissaries to woo Lee, but he refused to commit himself. If Myrtie was startled by the peculiar visitors smelling of beer and hair tonic who knocked at our front door, she made no mention of it; she knew Lee was capable of no guile. The threatening letters continuing to pour in the parsonage mail slot were not important either; Lee could take care of himself; he had since he was nine. Goodness, could you imagine Ike, now nearly that old, delivering telegrams in a saloon!

Only once did Lee lose his temper. One politician in our precinct boasted openly that if "that damned psalm singer won't stay in his pulpit where he belongs, I'll knock his block off personally!" Lee did not wait for chance to bring them together. One bright morning he walked into the boaster's office, announcing, tight-lipped, "Now's your chance to knock my block off. *If you can.* My name's Nies."

"I didn't mean anything, Father!" The politician took one look at Lee's six feet, the dangerous light in his eyes that turned steel-gray when he was angry, and held out a pudgy hand. "You know how you get carried away in the heat of a campaign. . . ." He looked so exactly like a sheep Myrtie had had for a pet in Texas that Lee laughed shortly, and turned upon his heel, leaving the other man to wonder what he had said that was so funny.

The campaign to eliminate Lee and his church constituency came to a violent climax a few weeks later.

"Come, quick! The church is burning down!" The cry and the pounding upon our front door woke us all about two in the morning. I remember how my hands shook so with cold though it was a warm night that I couldn't button my coat; and then I was running up the dark sidewalk with a pain in my side because I couldn't catch up with Dad's long, anxious strides. The church was blazing, all right; the highest flames were coming out of the vestry that had been fixed as a gym for the S.A.M.E.C.'s, out of the windows of the upstairs auditorium which had just been redecorated. *Whoever had set this was no stranger to the neighborhood; he'd waited until the fire would undo the patient work of months.*

"This is bad business, Mr. Nies." The fire chief, bulky in his rubber suit and big helmet, came striding up to Lee. He reported angrily, "We found rags soaked in kerosene in the vestry and the kitchen. This was set, damn it!"

So the letters hadn't been entirely "crackpot" after all. Dad just stared at him and then up at the tall church spire, where a fireman on a tall ladder was wetting down the roof. Would the whole church go? Would the work of nine years be consumed in a few terrible minutes? I remember shivering as the frightening flames burst through the roof and scarred the night sky red, and how the deep sad lines etched themselves into my father's face as he watched, helpless.

"If I'd stayed on my side of the tracks as I was warned, this might not have happened," Dad muttered. "But I didn't believe that people could fall so low." Surely this must be the work of some drunken tramp, Dad said. Trying to curry favor? It would be kinder to think him just a firebug.

Then his mouth hardened. As Dad lifted his fighting chin, the fear inside me suddenly was gone. Instead of the hissing water from the fire hose, I heard bright trumpets blowing, saw the charge of mighty gathering hosts in the leaping flames; and my father, standing there in his trousers pulled over his nightshirt with the wind blowing his fine hair, was clothed in shining armor of the spirit which neither fire nor sword could pierce.

"This is just what we needed!" Lee told the startled fire chief. "People will be so burned up over this the whole town will help us rebuild. This time we'll build it big enough for all our boys. We'll put in better showers, a running track in the gym. . . ."

The chief looked at this fighting parson who'd already rebuilt his church, bigger and better than ever, while it was still burning down, opened his mouth to speak and then closed it again. What was there to say to a man like that?

CHAPTER 8

The Other Side of Fear

"THE ONLY LEGACY a wise man leaves to his children is an education," Dad used to say to Ike and me. "And most of that is 'caught and not taught.' "

"Preachers' kids" are luckier than most because their father is at home so much more than parents who leave on the eight-ten every morning and do not return until the cocktail hour. Yet life in a Methodist parsonage forty years ago was full of so many things one could not do without "breaking the Sabbath"; we were not even allowed to ride on streetcars on Sunday because that would cause the conductor to work and so lose his lawful seventh day of rest. We used to listen to the five Roman Catholic children who lived next door to us, romping, playing, and screaming happily about their back yard after they got home from mass and we wished heartily our own Methodist Sabbath wasn't quite so brittle as to be broken up by a game of hopscotch.

Of course Ike and I had our Bible book, whose illustrations were so satisfactorily gory as to invest even the Sabbath with awesome drama. Daniel was in our Sunday book, walking about in his nightie, laying a careless hand upon the nose of a ferocious lion who was mostly all head and roar. Jonah, evacuating his unwanted tenant, still lingered in the whale's mouth, a fearful warning of what

97

happened to people who tried to get away from that piercing optic, the Eye of God, which saw right through everything—walls, houses, mountains—and even into the insides of whales.

But the picture we liked best was of Jesus talking to a group of children just like us. There was a little boy leaning against his knee, looking up into Jesus' face, and I remember thinking he was saying, "Will you take me fishing with you, the next time you go? Once I caught a fish *that big!*" And then Jesus would smile at him the way Dad did when we told a story we didn't expect him to believe. In the crook of the Master's arm . . . a pleasant place for a child to be. . . .

Calling a minister "narrow" because he has a set of standards in which he believes has always seemed incongruous to me. Some of the "narrowest" people I've ever known were those who insisted upon believing in nothing at all. They would be so afraid some-one would think them provincial or unsophisticated enough to believe in God, marriage for life, or in simple human loyalties that they wore themselves all out trying to keep an empty "open" mind. But try to shake them in their determination to be uncertain and see how pliable they were! They clung closer to their fetish of "broad-mindedness" than any Puritan father to his Blue Laws!

Ike and I had so many positive pleasures we did not much mind the negatives. Maybe after a leisurely breakfast we'd go out into the back yard with Dad to find a gorgeous black and gold butter-fly perched on one of Myrtie's yellow roses. "Isn't it nice how the Lord took so much pains with a little insect like that?" Dad mused. "What fun he must have had planning those delicate wings! Bot-tled gold from the sunshine and black traceries more intricate than the finest artistry [Dad never talked "down" to us children; we were supposed to talk "up" to him]woven in velvet too fragile to touch! All that trouble for a little creature that today is and tomorrow is not. It's almost as much of a miracle as a human soul."

Summers we went swimming together as a family, Mother and I clad in long black stockings and swimming suits with bloomers and a sailor collar, a getup so bulky when wet that it was all we could do to jump up and down in the water. But we'd sit on the sand and sing at the top of our lungs.

"Mary had a William goat," Dad would begin, his eyes twinkling and Ike and I would join in breathlessly, "William goat, William goat!" Then Mother and all of us would announce gaily, "His stomach was lined with zinc!" When we beat the shabby parsonage carpet in the back yard we would sing,

"*My Father is rich in houses and lands,*
He holdeth the wealth of the worlds in His hands. . . ."

and never know we were poor. We knew for a fact we were royalty. Whenever we got ready to go to a birthday party, I all decked out in a starched white dress and Ike in clean short pants, Mother would always remind us, "Now hold up your chins and remember, you're children of a King!" No inferiority complexes there, if the other children always did have more expensive clothes than we did.

Another thing Mother taught us was never to give up a project once we'd started. Frequently when she'd send us to find a book or a lost sock we'd come back saying, childlike, we couldn't find it. "Then go right back and make it!" Mother would order sternly. We usually found what we were looking for then. We took all of our fun as a family, rather than using home merely as a place from which to taxi to Cub Scouts or the neighborhood movies.

One winter as Ike and I grew older, Dad made a big "double-runner" by putting boards across the Flexible Flyers that my brother and I had outgrown, and after Wednesday-night prayer meetings we would invite half a dozen young people to fill up the sled, to go sweeping down the moon-silver snowy hill on Morton Street. As you walked back up the mile-long hill, tingling all over with the crisp air and the heavenly rush of flying down, you sang with the happiness of just being alive. But one Saturday night we nearly disrupted the church by not getting back home to the parsonage till half-past twelve. "Carousing on the Sabbath!" as one old maid (he happened to be a masculine one) expostulated, shocked, to Dad.

"Well, if David could dance before the Lord, I guess maybe He wouldn't begrudge the minister's family a little coasting," Dad said.

Often Dad took Ike and me calling with him after school. When our old Dodge with the cathedral windows of isinglass in the back turned into a street, all the children would come running, for they knew that Dad always kept a bag of candy in his bulging, shabby, blue coat pocket. Once when he was doling out the pieces to Protestant, Jew, and Catholic children alike, one little girl protested, "But you're *my* minister!"

"The candy isn't Methodist," Dad twinkled. The children would never let Dad leave after he'd completed his calls indoors upon the grownups, without "making the puppy bark." His blue eyes would twinkle as he put his hands up over his mouth and the most convincing whines, growls, and barks would issue, with the children jumping up and down, crying, "Do it again. Please do it again!" Thus I learned what it meant, "Except ye become as a little child . . ." Religion didn't belong only to Sunday service; it was joyful any day in the week to serve the Lord as Dad did.

We children learned early that all the parsonage problems were ours too and we must do something about them. It was always very exciting when we moved to a new parish to find out what the president of the Ladies' Aid was like, because from her all blessings flowed. She it was who counted the cups the former preacher's kids had cracked and decided what new equipment the parsonage might need. It was supposed to be fully furnished before the minister's family moved in, but frequently there were hiatuses. If the Ladies' Aid president was a fussy soul who didn't like children, we had to walk like Agag, delicately; but most of these good ladies had a saving sense of humor.

Once when Ike was four, the president came when Mother was away to ask what was needed at the parsonage; but Ike enlightened her.

"Our mommy wants a new carpet for the front parlor because the one in there's a horror," Ike announced. "But if she can't get that, she'd like new curtains. And if she can't get *that*, she'll *take* a new teakettle!" The Ladies'-Aider laughed so hard that we were granted all three wishes.

As soon as we children could toddle, we were made to feel that we "belonged" to the church and the church to us, as much as to any grownup. After its symbolism had been explained to us, we were even taken up to the communion rail by Mother, who otherwise couldn't have gone. But the young worshipers had their difficulties. Once on the way up the aisle Ike broadcast loudly, "Mommy, I just pulled a tooth!" and had to be led, bloody, away. Another time when Myrtie heard smothered giggles, she turned around to find me trailing her up the aisle with my new blue-silk parasol opened over my proud head. But even that early a real sense of the universality of all worship seeped through to Ike and me. Now when I go up to the Blessed Table, I see my Dad's worn but well-polished black boots coming toward my bent gaze, hear his voice saying softly, "This is your Father's table. All ye who are in love and charity with your neighbors and a lover of Him are welcome, no matter what your creed. . . ."

We preacher's kids even had a part in "making Dad's sermon," by keeping quiet until he was finished. So long as we could hear the clatter of his ancient typewriter, which he banged with two fingers, all voices and steps were muffled. When Dad got to a tricky part, the typewriter would stop and we would listen anxiously to the tramp, tramp of his feet on the worn study carpet, back and forth, back and forth llamalike, until the typewriter would bang again triumphantly and we'd all breathe easier. Finally the study door would bang open and Dad would call, "Anyone around here besides me want an ice-cream cone?" We'd rush at him, screaming madly, knowing the sermon was "made" for another week.

But, perhaps strangely, Dad would never let Ike and me attend any of the funerals at our church. Birth and death were both juiceless words to us until our little brother, Bildad, was born. Dad joked before he came, "Myrtie, your father's second name is 'William' and we don't want to disappoint him; but I would like the new baby named 'Dad' for me." So though we all knew that if the baby was a boy he'd be christened Lee Nies, Jr., the name Bildad stuck for everyday. It makes all the difference in the world how you say a name, gently, haughtily, or chuckling; the way Dad said "Bildad" it meant "Sonny."

Ike and I were never shown movies, months in advance, of a queer embryonic blob curled up in our mother's stomach, to prepare us for the miracle of Bildad's birth. But we watched my mother get ready the flower-sprigged bassinet and sing under her breath as she feather-stitched the pink-satin edge, for the new baby was very welcome. Ike and I merely spent the night at a neighbor's and when we came home, Bildad was there, wrapped in the pink-edged blanket and winking his blue eyes very fast. Ike looked dubiously at the nurse bathing Bildad's little pink squirming body and wondered how long it would be before he could play baseball?

"Take his hand, Susie," my mother beamed. It curled over mine, soft and warm and real at last. All I could think of to say as the joy of my new brother's clinging hand welled up in me was, "He's got real fingernails!"

Then suddenly, four days later, the Lord took Bildad away again. When Ike and I got home from school that day, Doc Mason's old black car was in front of our house and we found the same neighbor with whom we'd stayed when Bildad was born, crying in our kitchen. Up over our heads frightening, hurrying footsteps were going back and forth between our mother's room and the bathroom.

"You're to come home with me and not bother your ma and dad," the good neighbor told us. "Your little brother's dead."

"Will he be put in a gray box?" Ike asked, horrified. The father of our five friends next door, a policeman, had died suddenly last month; and Ike and I had watched the funeral start, from our hidden nook behind the barberry bushes on our front lawn. We hardly knew our five friends as they walked down their own front steps, dressed in dark new clothes, their eyes red and swollen, and got in beside their black-draped mother in the first car of the funeral procession. That wall of strangeness had thickened while Ike and I, breathless, watched strangers in black gloves carry a long gray box out the front door, walking as if it were heavy, as if they were sorry for what they were doing. We knew what was inside, and as the carriage filled with flowers crawled by us, the sickish smell of death was in our nostrils.

"I hate funerals!" Ike gasped. "I'm never going to die!"

"You will," I assured him gloomily. "Everybody does. Do you

suppose dead people go back to the same place that babies come from?" And now little Bildad would be nailed shut in a horrible, breathless gray box, too. I burst into tears, demanding, "Was Bildad sick?"

"Doc Mason doesn't know yet what was wrong with him. The nurse was bathing him in your mother's room and the baby just turned blue and died," the neighbor related, wiping her eyes. "Now come along home with me, children. I've made some fresh cookies."

Bildad had turned blue! I felt sick to my stomach but of course Ike and I had to go with her; we even accepted woodenly the cookies she offered, but we could not eat. We promised to play quietly in the back yard, but as soon as she was gone indoors I lost my lunch behind the blackberry bush and felt better. "I'm going home to find Dad," I told Ike. "I think it's all a lie. Bildad never turned blue! You stay here and make a noise now and then like we're playing, and then I'll come back and tell you the truth."

No one noticed me as I crept back into our too-still kitchen and up the back stairs. There was no sound anywhere; the doctor must have gone and the nurse must be with Mother behind the closed bedroom door. Then I heard a voice. Dad's study door was shut too, but there must be someone in there with him, for I could hear Dad talking. I crept up the carpeted stairs, squatted down by the study door, making myself as small as possible, to listen.

"You don't need Myrtie like I do!" Dad was crying. "Why, we've belonged to each other ever since we were six and seven when I built her our first house in a chinaberry tree. . . . *I just can't go on without her!* My son is dead and Thy will be done. *But don't take Myrtie too!*"

The agony of Dad's voice went through me, sharp and hurting, and I knew who was in there with him. Dad was wrestling with the angel of the Lord as Jacob had wrestled, hopelessly, smitten hip and thigh, but never giving up. "You were there at our wedding," Dad reminded the Lord. "You *gave* her to me. You can't take her away, not yet. The children need her. You can't possibly need her the way we do. . . ." When he stopped, I knew, frozen with cold, that my mother was going to die, for Dad was giving her up. He gasped, "Nevertheless, not my will, but Thine. . . ."

"Dad. Dad!" Panic made me reckless. I beat on the study door, crying hysterically, "Let me in!"

The study door opened at once. Dad gathered me up in his big arms and there was peace in the way he held me, a safe, grand peace that only those know who have been cradled in the Everlasting Arms of Him who is a Father too.

"Your mother will live, Susie," Dad said. He was so sure that I was sure, too, but I hid my face in his shoulder, sobbing, "But Bildad's dead!"

"Yes," he agreed, not trying to deny anything. "The Lord loaned him to us for only a little while. Would you like to see him?"

I didn't want to see Bildad dead in a long gray box but Dad carried me into the next bedroom and lifted my chin gently so I had to look. Why, Bildad wasn't blue at all! He was just asleep in his flower-sprigged bassinet. He was lying there with his eyes closed, and his little hand with the tiny perfect fingernails was curled up outside the soft pink-edged blanket my mother had made for him as she sang. Dad spoke to Bildad exactly as if he could hear.

"You'll leave a lonesome place in this house, son, for all that you were here only four days."

Dad smiled at Bildad and then at me and I knew a wonderful thing—*there was nothing to be afraid of*. Death was only a beloved baby, asleep in his bassinet.

People thought it queer of Dad that Ike and I were not at our brother's funeral. We went to school as usual, and when we came home, Bildad and his bassinet were gone; Mother was asleep up in her room; and Dad himself got us our supper. Everything would now be the same as it used to be before Bildad came and went home to the Lord, I thought, in vast relief.

But nothing was the same, actually. Myrtie lived but she did not get well; the mysterious fever no doctor could seem to diagnose hung on and on; and she grew weaker and weaker, for there is no successful operation for a broken heart, nor can peace of mind be poured out of a bottle. It almost seemed as if Mother had gone away with Bildad, she was so changed. Day after day she grew thinner until she hardly pushed up the blanket at all on the bed when we went into her room to say "good morning" or "good night," which was practically all we children saw of her, for the sound of our running feet was like riveting in her ears and the slam of a door made her cry out in pain.

"She doesn't mean to be cross," Dad would explain when she scolded us for making a racket. "She just—isn't herself yet." But it was hard to remember at six and three to walk quietly all day every day; the sickroom was darkened and so full of such queer smells that Ike and I got out of there as soon as we could; so Myrtie cried and said that her children didn't love her any more. One dreadful day she picked up her hand mirror and broke into tears, sobbing to Dad, "I'm so ugly! You can't love me either, this way!" Dad shut the bedroom door so Ike and I couldn't hear any more; but next day he bought her a pile of frilly nightgowns though his own shirts were ragged at collar and cuffs.

Myrtie lay in bed for five dreadful years, and all this time Lee never once admitted that she wouldn't get well or that caring for her was a drain upon him. But after the nurse left—you couldn't pay one for long on the $1600-a-year salary—Dad had to do everything for his sick wife; feed, clothe, and discipline two growing, bewildered children; and act as pastor of his rapidly expanding church. He'd prepare his sermons while he was getting breakfast, and we'd hear him muttering, "My text for this morning is 'I will lift up mine eyes unto the hills,' " while he was stirring the oatmeal. Deep lines etched themselves down the sides of Dad's mouth and his lips began to twitch in and out for no reason; but he always got us off to school and was there when we came home. Then he'd do his parish calling, while we were at home to answer the sickroom bell.

When spring came around, Dad took off the storm windows and put them all around our little upstairs veranda to make a sun room where Mother's bed could be set. But the worst trial was that she could now hear when the same curious woman neighbor came every few days to ask us children, avidly, "Is your Ma dead yet?"

Myrtie always said that Ike saved her life by his angry answer one morning. "No!" Ike said. "And she isn't going to die! You go home!"

Finally friends in the parish saw that Lee's own health would break if he didn't have some help, so they banded together to hire him a maid. Annie was supposed to do all the washing, ironing, cooking, and caring for two lively children at the magnificent salary of five dollars a week. She was a good woman and a fine cook, but we kids did wish she'd wash her long coil of black greasy hair more often and that all her house dresses were not dark gray with black figures, so as not to show the spots. Mother used to wear pink, blue, and red house dresses with ruffles at her throat and when she stirred a cake, she sang about "La Paloma," the gay dove. But the worst thing was having to listen to Annie talk endlessly about her twin nieces, "May 'n Lily." May wore a blue ribbon in her hair and Lily a pink one, to tell them apart; but they were as different from us as night and day; they never, never talked back or dirtied their clothes. How Ike and I loathed them! If ever we met up with those loathsome paragons, we'd tear up the ribbons so they'd get mixed up, we decided fiercely, and roll them both in the mud. Fortunately, we never met.

It was when I had the measles that Dad first introduced me to the "Hallelujah Chorus." Since the shades in my room had to be down and I could neither read nor scribble in my "poetry notebook," a parishioner had contributed her ancient gramophone to amuse me. The machine had an enormous fluted horn and round waxlike records which fitted over a turning cylinder as each squeaked, "Edison Record!" before any music happened. Dad dug up somewhere some Handel records, and every time the machine squawked tinnily "Hallelujah!" Dad would stand erect by my bed till the record was finished.

"Why are you standing up?" I demanded, so he told me about George II's rising in tribute to the King of Kings. After that I stood up too in my long white flannel nightgown, with my face covered with spots, but with my heart standing tall and straight and beautiful beside the King of England and my Dad.

Thus, during those formative years, Ike and I caught much deeper learning from Dad than was written in books. He never considered it necessary to go into a detailed anatomical lecture to explain to us children the facts of life, nor did he think the honest mistakes of youth comical. Once when I was twelve, I was put, after an emergency operation, into the maternity ward to recuperate—and refused to come home until I was delivered of *my* baby too.

"I don't care if it's black or white," I sobbed to the great laughter of all the listening nurses. "Everyone else got a baby here!"

But Dad was grave as he promised me, "You'll get your baby, Susie; and his face will be white because yours is. But a baby's as much spirit as body, and I don't know what color his soul will be. All I know is it will be clean and shining, fresh from God . . . the Lord love him, as I will!" (When my son was born years later, it was not the physical pain I remembered as I looked at his tiny, red, little face; I saw only his soul "clean and shining, fresh from God . . . the Lord love him, as I will.")

Dad must have had more hands than one of those Buddhist idols for he juggled all his duties, and still the church grew and prospered. He preached three times on Sundays, morning, evening, and leading the Nies Club was really another sermon. He'd park us Sunday afternoons at Junior League so he could get in a few calls, and often took us to prayer meetings so Annie could have a night off. He didn't leave us at home alone for fear Ike would blow up the house with his new chemical kit or I would get deep in a book and leave Mother's soup burning on the stove. It was during those allopathic doses of religion that I perfected my technique for turning off my attention when the sermon began, to make up a story of my own; often I got so enthralled when the lions were roaring after my fleeing heroine that Ike would have to kick me in the shin to get me up for the hymns.

But more often I would listen to what Dad had to say, for our minds worked in so much the same way that I frequently knew what he was going to say before he said it. Once when he hesitated for a word, I supplied it loudly from the front pew. On the way home he asked how I had known what he was going to say.

"Oh, I can think in your mind," I told him airily.

He looked a little frightened. "I guess I'll have to be more careful."

Dad always stayed home on Thursday afternoons when Annie

went to see the paragon twins, so he could hear Mother's bell if she rang, which was how I happened to hear what he and Molly Stark said that day when she came running in our front door, calling, "Lee! Where are you? I've got to see you!" All the young people in our church called Dad "Lee," and he liked it. Molly was the soprano soloist in our church choir and usually her voice sounded like a silver flute, but today it was shrill and scared.

"Lee," Molly gasped, "I'm going to die!"

I was studying about Hannibal's crazy elephants but my hand froze on the Latin book; both Molly and Dad were too intent to see that my bedroom door, right next to the study, was open, too.

"Sit down and relax, Molly," Dad said quietly. "We all are."

You could hear the rumble of the chair as he pushed it out for her, the big comfortable leather chair where he put very special visitors; and then he began to talk to give Molly time to get hold of herself. "You know Reba Black, Molly?" Everybody knew Reba; she washed for all the people on our street, including the Starks who lived a block above us. "I buried her baby today. His name was Sammy—Sammy Black. Pickaninnies are prettier than little white babies, I always think. . . . Reba had him dressed in a very clean sugar sack and she cried, 'He'll be col' in the ground, Mister Nies, without any shirt!' So I came back and got some of Bildad's things from up attic. Sammy looked cute as a bug when we got him all dressed up with a warm sweater and a little white woolly hat. Reba was pleased. But she said, 'Don't let them throw no dirt on him, Mr. Nies. He's too little for that!' So we didn't put little Sammy into the casket at all; I carried him in my arms to the cemetery and then laid Sammy into his little box into the ground myself. I told his father, 'Go home and tell Reba that I just smoothed the warm earth over like a blanket. . . .'"

"Lee, Lee, you're wonderful!" Molly's voice broke in, calmer now, and as it ought to be. "You're the most compassionate man I ever saw!" There was a warm silence between them and then she told him that she had cancer of the throat; the doctor had just told her that if she lived four months, she'd be lucky. "I don't mind—very much—about myself. But I can't leave Jimmy!"

Jimmy was her ten-year-old son who sang in our junior choir. He had a lovely voice, almost as high as his mother's, a boy's clear soprano. Last Sunday had been Easter and Jimmy had stood up there in our choir loft and sung, "I know that my Redeemer liveth." He was tall for his ten years, with white-gold hair and blue eyes, and he'd been almost unearthly beautiful standing there in his white robe while his voice soared up and up. When he'd finished, a sigh had run over the congregation as if they were sorry to drop back into the pews from the high place where Jimmy had taken them.

His mother said, "He's so young yet, Lee. And his father. . . ." There was a short silence before she said honestly, "He's a good man but he's never grown up. It makes me worry. . . ."

"I'll make a bargain with you, Molly!" Lee interrupted. Unbelievably he began to chuckle. "I'll look after your Jimmy if you'll ride herd on my Bildad. Glory be, Bildad must be five by now; old enough to go to school—kindergarten anyway. When you see him, you tell him his Pop said you were to look over his report card, and if he's got any D's, you give him what for!"

"Lee, Lee"—Molly was laughing and crying at the same time. "It's a bargain. You make it all seem so—so—everyday. Funny, you know everyone has to die, but you never expect it to happen to you."

"What people forget is that we're living in eternity right now," Lee reminded her. "The Lord holds the past and the present and the future—and all families, wherever they are—together, safe in His hand. When you believe that, you can go on."

"Yes," Molly whispered so low I could hardly hear her. "Now I can go on. But I want you to promise me something. When I— when the time comes—will you be there to tell Jimmy about our bargain? Will you?"

"Of course I'll be there," Lee told her. "Any time, night or day. Don't you worry." When they went by my open door, they were walking hand in hand toward the front door and Molly was smiling. It was a kind of white smile, but it was there.

My mother's little silver bell began to ring furiously and I went in to see what she wanted. She was very thin and her skin was yellow and her eyes were no longer blue but almost black. She asked, "Who was that? In the study?" She couldn't bear not knowing all that was going on, being shut out; and yet if you told her all that was happening, you never could tell how she'd take it, whether she'd be angry or hurt. It was usually one or the other because she was "not herself."

I told her, "Molly Stark came in to talk about Jimmy. She—she's worried about him. And Dad promised to see what he could do."

"Oh," my mother said relieved, "was that all? Tell your father I want him to read to me. My head aches."

"I can read to you," I told her proudly.

"No, I want Lee," she said fretfully. She kept him reading all the rest of the afternoon till he was so hoarse he could hardly speak.

It was small wonder that one Sunday morning Lee woke up to find that he couldn't remember a word of the sermons he'd prepared for that day. One of his friends had to rush out from Boston to preach for him.

"Complete physical and nervous exhaustion," old Doc Mason growled. He was a thick tub of a man, with a thatch of gray hair, spectacles that he put on and took off, and an elk's tooth dangling on his rounded stomach; but somehow just seeing him stump into the sickroom and thump his black bag down on the floor, made you feel better. He was extremely profane, but no one minded, for his heart was bigger than he was. He told Lee, "I've seen this coming. You blankety-blank fool, do you think you've got pin feathers already? You're human too. You've got to go away for a complete rest." He marched to the telephone, called up two of our church's official board, and then marched back again to announce that Lee was sailing for Bermuda in two days and not to argue. Forget the blankety-blank family; they'd be all right.

Lee was too tired to argue; in fact, he was so tired he hardly knew when the ship sailed. Which of his friends had tucked the money and ticket under his pillow, he neither knew nor cared, for he was already asleep. He slept most of the voyage and when he woke up, he was lying on the warm Bermuda sands under a hot sun, wishing he never had to move again. His mind had cleared, but it seemed as if he never could take up again the burden of Myrtie's sickness. He was so tired, tired, tired. . . . He lay there on the hot sand for three weeks, relaxing every taut nerve, listening to the surf whisper or roar along the shore. There was a rhythm to the waves' coming and going almost like words.

"A bruiséd reed shall he not break; a smoking flax shall he not quench. . . ."

Over and over the promise the waves were chanting echoed in his weary head. It was true that up to now the strength to live along from day to day had been granted him, but just holding on by your teeth was not enough. Why hadn't he been able to help himself to complete sanity as he had helped Molly Stark? "Physician, heal thyself. . . ." *What had happened to his faith?* As Lee lay there on the sand, washed by despair, Molly's words came back to him. . . . "Compassionate," she'd called you; it meant suffering with someone. If it hadn't been for losing Bildad, you'd never have known the right words to comfort Molly and Reba Black. You never really understood sorrow till you'd plumbed its dark depths yourself. Maybe the same thing was true of faith; only by having the choking waves of doubt wash over you could you struggle through to the firm ground of a faith that could not be shaken, have something real to give your people.

As the healing days went by, Lee grew more and more sure that he had found the right answer; that nothing is wasted, not suffering, pain, despair, not even death, if these things deepen your capacity for living greatly. *You can share what you have yourself.* This explained even the Crucifixion, Lee saw reverently, for it was through the agony of the final separation from his Father that the Lord had become one with the suffering, lonely thief on the cross beside His. Only compassionate love, a suffering with, can cast out fear.

"I've been afraid," Lee knew. "Afraid of so many things."

Lying there listening to the eternal whisper of the sea that gives back what is in a man's inner mind, Lee faced his naked, honest self for the first time, and knew that he had not really meant it when he told the Lord to use His own will about taking Myrtie. *He'd been afraid that the Lord would take him at his word.* It was his own fear that had worn him out, his fear for Myrtie, for the

children, for the church. He had been afraid to trust the promises
of God that He would care for His own. . . . That was what
had happened to his faith. . . . Seeing clearly at last what his
mistake had been, Lee thrust it from him, now and forever. He
knew, exultantly, *there can be no lasting peace until you come
through on the other side of fear. The other side of fear is glory
—and God.*

"I'm going home," Lee knew, sitting up suddenly on the sand.

Rested in mind and body, he took the next ship back to Boston,
and every reverberation of the homing engines was chanting his
new knowledge. Little children, he saw, knew no fear, nor did
very old people; one was too recently arrived to worry and the
other knew it was no use; that was why young and old children
were such fun to be with. When you could thumb your nose at
fear, you were as free as . . . as good salt air!

Leaning over the ship's railing, with the sea wind tossing his
wild hair, Lee wanted to cry his amazing discovery to the universe.
Cry it to those stars up there, to the winds that blow in dark spaces.
*"There's nothing in this world or the next to be afraid of! The
promises of the Lord are true!"* Cry it to people in tenements, in
hospitals, in prisons. . . . Cry it to lonely mothers beside empty
cribs, asking, "Why? Why?" as you had done. Cry it to Molly
Stark about to die. *"There really is a peace that passes understanding.
I know. I've found it!"*

From the day of his vibrant return, new life blew through our
whole family. Even Myrtie suddenly felt better and sat up in a
wheelchair, and with her practiced hands upon the machinery,
our household began to move more smoothly. Meals were on time
and we children liked to come home from school; Lee could catch
up on his parish calling, which had fallen sadly behind. Before
long Myrtie was even walking a few steps by herself, every day a
little farther, determined at last to get well, so that the color came
back to her cheeks and the roundness to her lovely body. It seemed
as if by conquering his own fear for her and by really surrendering
her future to the Lord, Lee had passed on to Myrtie his own secret
of returning health.

"I've stopped praying the Lord to make me well," Myrtie told

Lee dreamily. "I just say now, 'Lord, I belong to you. Whatever you want for me is right.' And every day I feel better!" In her surrender, strangely she had found triumph.

Lee trailed his laughter like a banner into other sickrooms. He seldom asked any more how a patient felt; he merely told them stories about what was going on in the parish. Or if there was a piano or organ handy, he'd sit down, play a lively march that would set even bed-weary fingers and feet tapping; or perhaps he'd throw back his bright head and sing in his golden tenor:

> "*I had a horse by the name of Napoleon*
> *All on account of its bony part . . .*"

Then when he had everyone relaxed and smiling, his rippling fingers would slide easily into his mother Bowitt's favorite song:

> "*This is the Lord's great day,*
> This is the Lord's great day!"

All life was glorious, a hymn to Almighty God, for *his Myrtie was getting well!* Lee's text for our morning prayers and for his sermon on Sunday morning when Myrtie was able to go with him to church for the first service in six years was so big he said it ought to be sung by the Handel and Haydn Society instead of being just read; "The morning stars sang together and all the sons of God shouted for joy!"

Then one night Lee's summons came to keep his promise to Molly Stark about her Jimmy. It was one o'clock in the morning when Molly's frantic husband came pounding upon our front door, gasping, "Come quick, Mr. Nies. Doc says that Molly's going!" Lee flung on his clothes, and their footsteps were loud under my bedroom window as he and Jimmy's father ran up the empty sidewalk. As they neared the Stark house, Dad told us later, every window was lighted and the front door wide open and down the stairs came the sound of singing:

"*I know that my Redeemer liveth. . . .*"

"I don't see how Jimmy can do it!" his father gasped. "But Molly asked him to. She said she wanted to hear it again. I don't see. . . ."

But Lee was already halfway up the stairs. The bedroom into which he looked was filled with light. Molly, her body so thin it barely lifted the sheet, was lying there with her eyes closed. Old Doc Mason was sitting beside the bed, holding her wrist and scowling down at his big old-fashioned watch; he always hated losing a patient. And holding onto the iron foot of his mother's bed stood frightened, ten-year-old Jimmy, singing his heart out.

> *"I know that my Redeemer liveth*
> *And that He shall stand in that latter day*
> *Upon the earth. . . ."*

Suddenly as he gasped, and stopped, his sobs breaking through, Lee's golden tenor took up the song. He came from the doorway, slid his warm arm about the boy's shoulders, and smiled into Molly's opening, tired eyes. After an instant Jimmy's relieved silver soprano soared again too and together he and Lee sang on:

> *"For now is Christ risen from the dead. . . ."*

Molly's face, smiling at Lee and her son, was radiant. Lee was there, keeping his promise, so now she could let go. . . . As her tired, heavy eyelids flickered down, Doc Mason snapped shut his watch, and laid her hand back on the bed; but Jimmy didn't know that his mother was gone. He and Lee went on singing. They sang till the whole room was filled with music that swelled and swelled till it burst the low bedroom ceiling, swept out into the listening night, soared up and up beyond the stars, singing Molly Stark home.

CHAPTER 9

Beautiful Newagen

DAD USED TO CHUCKLE that Newagen was as near heaven as anyone was likely to get in this life, for on its rocky east shore lived seven ministers and a man named Lord! Land was cheap, though the rugged shore line with pointed pines pricking the sky was as beautiful as when later it would cost from ten to fifty times as much. What Lee loved about this east coast of Southport Island were not only its yellow Maine rocks and crashing sea, but its immensity—there was enough of everything, sea, sky, and the salty air that, he insisted, would breathe new life into dry bones. Often after preaching Sunday evenings Lee would drive all night just to see the sun rise out of the sea at Newagen, in rosy splendor and vast solitude. Looking out from his cottage veranda across the waking sea he could see only a few islands—Fisherman, White, and Squirrel—and beyond, a gray ghost along the horizon twenty miles away, lay Monhegan; but beyond that was only open sea where you could sail and sail unhindered till you bumped into Spain. For the first time since he'd left the vast rolling plains of Texas, Lee had found a place big enough to call "home."

"The Snuggery," which he bought for Myrtie at Newagen, was their first real home since they'd climbed together into their chinaberry tree house; the only place in the world where they could go inside (as Myrtie said "alone, together"), shut the door, and not open it again till they felt like it. Like all ministers' families, they lived with one foot halfway out the front door. At any hour of the day or night, the telephone would ring and Lee would be off to comfort the sick, to bail out a boy who'd been arrested, or even to spend the night in jail, standing by a parishioner arrested for murder. Lee had no privacy and pitifully few possessions—his books, his clothes, Myrtie's secondhand piano, my two-hundred-year-old cradle, and assorted odds and ends. At Snuggery half the chairs were wobbly and the table a packing box; but the sea sang around its front door so loudly you could pretend not to hear a knock if you wanted to; and, glory be, the only telephone was a quarter of a mile away, down the road in E. Gray's store.

"Newagen's really a state of mind," Lee used to tell Myrtie happily. "A state of peace."

They called their first home "The Snuggery" because it was such a snug fit for us four; the living room was small, boxlike, and darkened by the surrounding veranda; the tiny kitchenette was almost completely filled by a rusty three-burner oil stove and the leaky icebox; while upstairs was merely an open unfinished loft to sleep in, with windows at each end. But the screened veranda where you really lived had a vast, uncluttered view of the sea where lobster boats sputtered at dawn and where ships on their way to Boothbay Harbor curtsied in the wind. At night, the only visitor you had to let in was the long bright finger of the Cuckolds Lighthouse that swept across your pillow as you lay abed, saying, "Go to sleep. I'll watch!"

"We're land barons!" Lee told Myrtie, sweeping her into his arms where he could hold her as long as he wanted without any parishioner barging in. "Every board in this house is ours, dear!" He looked up at the ceiling, chuckling ruefully. "Every crack!" They grinned happily at each other.

We children throve here mightily. Sunburned and salty-haired, we came indoors only to eat, leaped like chamois over the rocky shore, and when the tide came in over the sun-warmed rocks, so that the temperature in the cove was not actually freezing, we swam with Dad. "Susie," Myrtie groaned to me, "not a third dish of 'clam muddle'! You'll burst!"

"Oh, let her," Lee urged. "It'll be a happy death."

Replete with "clam muddle" and the happiness of being alone, we sat together on our veranda and watched the pink reflection when the sun went down and the stars swam up out of the dark sea. "You see that biggest star up there, kids?" Lee would ask. "That's where I'm going to build a mansion for your mother someday."

"Well, all I ask is that it'll have an electric stove," Myrtie sighed. All her life she'd been wrestling with worn-out parsonage stoves: wood stoves, oil stoves, ancient popping gas stoves; but they had all one thing in common—you had to black them, which was, to the fastidious Myrtie, a grievous chore. "A big, white-enamel stove, brand new and paid for!" she stipulated as her idea of heaven.

"I gotta stove, you gotta stove, all God's chillun's got stoves!" Lee began to sing gaily. "When we get to heben, gonna cook all around. . . ." Instantly the rest of us chimed in—Myrtie's soprano, my alto, Ike's voice that cracked now and then because it was changing from a boy's soprano to baritone—"Gonna cook all ober God's heben!"

At Newagen we burst into song whenever we wanted to without worrying about disturbing the neighbors, the squirrels, or lobsters. Dad would be painting an old chair on the veranda and would begin; then Mother would chime in from the tiny kitchen where she was making biscuits; Ike would run for his banjo; and I'd stick in my two cents' worth from upstairs where I was reading a book. We were the singingest family. We sang everything from Handel's *Messiah* to "Brighten the Corner Where You Are"; we sang until the star where Dad was going to build Mother her mansion with the white-enamel electric stove was high overhead in the night sky before we stumbled to bed, intoxicated with our own music and with peace.

The Newagen people delighted Lee even more than the view from his front veranda, for they reminded him of his boyhood. They were soft-spoken as a Texan is, though they slurred their words differently. They shot out no street lights from sheer ex-

uberance, but their humor was deep and irrepressible, popping out
in queer geysers of action when you least expected it. And both
Texans and Maine people were completely and stubbornly themselves.

"Chips off the Maine granite, these lobster men are," Lee told
Myrtie, admiringly. "With all the sharp edges left on. Once they
make up their minds to a thing, you can't change them either, any
more than a rock." He paused. "I don't want to change them, just
to know them."

Lee would sit for hours on the shore beside a lobster man who
was painting his dory and say nothing. The neighbor would slap
on paint busily while Lee was equally busy looking out to sea that
was now jade, now violet, now soft, moving gray, as a cloud passed
over. Finally another lobster man would chug up to the nearby
fish pier from hauling his traps, and the gulls would swoop down
in a white-winged, screaming, hungry crowd.

"Some cute to watch, ain't they?" The lobster man would pause
in his painting to admire, hooking his thumb at the gulls, swooping,
whirling, snatching, all with infinite grace, a rush of snowy wings
and bright orange beaks. "Some smart, too. Mother walks off 'n
leaves 'em soon's they're born, so they gotta be. Hear that one
laugh? Just like that fat lady from the hotel. They can take a burlap
bag off a bait tub even when it's tied, with them beaks."

Then and then only, when he'd been invited, would Lee speak.
"Is lobstering very dangerous? I mean, can you go out all winter?"

"Well, yes and no. Gits a little mite choppy sometimes." The
Maine man admitted winter nor'easters. "Still, my folks been
lobsterin' hereabouts goin' on a hundred years. Grandpop was
drownded off Horn Point. Pop was drownded too. Something ate
him; all we ever found was an arm, but we knew it by the tattooed
marks. Buried it over there in the cemetery, but most of him's still
at sea. You heard tell o' the big blow up to the Bay of Fundy when
eighty men from Southport was lost? Pretty near all that was old
enough to go to sea was drownded." He meditated. Slap, slap went
the paint brush. He shifted his heavy boots, spat into the ripple of
the incoming tide, and finally added, "But their sons grew up." It
went without saying that they went to sea too.

All native Newagen seethed with fury when one of the summer women started a "Village Improvement Society." "Why don't they go improve Boston or New York if they're so sot on it?" Captain E. Gray, who ran the post office and village store, demanded angrily of Lee. "Them places ain't got room to spit in, let alone live in decent." But improve Newagen? The very idea made him apoplectic.

Lee agreed with him. "Those people know how to live," he told Myrtie as he lay beside her on a rock, soaking up sun and peace. "They don't hurry, whatever the provocation; and if they want to take time out from earning a living to enjoy something, they do. Know where I found old Cap'n Gray yesterday afternoon when his daughter Mary sent me to look for him because it was mail time? Sitting out on the fish pier looking at the sunset. 'Some handsome, ain't it?' " he asked me, dreamily. "He knew mail would keep but the sunset wouldn't."

"Bubs," as the villagers called Captain E. Gray, ran his store to suit himself also, and if anyone didn't like his way, they could go somewhere else. When he bought a batch of flour or cereal, Bubs kept it until it was sold; but he never raised the price. If he bought a can of salmon to sell for twenty cents, he sold it for that no matter how the war sent prices soaring. That would have been profiteering, and he was as honest as sunlight. He didn't hold with being rushed. Once when the summer people clamored for fruit and fresh vegetables, against his better judgment, Bubs invested in a big bunch of bananas. The news went all up and down the shore, "Bubs has some fruit!" But by the time Lee got to the store, none was left.

"No, I ain't got no bananas and what's more I ain't gonna git no more," Bubs announced grimly. "I couldn't keep 'em in the store ten minutes!"

"He's like Moses," Lee thought delightedly, looking up at the captain's big six-foot body, his shrewd blue eyes behind their steel-rimmed spectacles. "As long as he can help it, the children of Newagen won't run after any golden calves! But stick to good, plain manna."

Bubs wouldn't sell you anything, either, unless he was convinced you needed it. After a stormy week when Ike's rubbers developed gaping holes, Lee went down to the store to see if Bubs had any in stock. He found the old man perched on a high stool behind the mail window making out "them tormented reports for them fool Nosy Parkers up in Washington." Bubs was breathing heavily, digging the stub of his pencil into the paper while Lee waited patiently for several minutes. Finally he asked, "Got any rubbers for Ike, Bubs?"

The old man didn't answer, just went on writing.

"But, Bubs, Ike needs rubbers or he may get pneumonia!" Lee insisted.

"Trouble 'n dogfish 'n summer boarders all come to oncet, seems like," Bubs remarked irritably, throwing down his pencil. "Sartin I got rubbers, but I ain't gonna sell you any. I sat down for a couple o' hours, figurin' what everyone here'll need in the village come winter, John Snowman and his kids 'n the Gamage young ones and the rest. If you think I'm goin' through all that again. . . . Oh, well, if Ike needs 'em. . . ." He waved a defeated hand at Lee. "Go on up attic 'n pick out a pair if you got to. And don't fall over nuthin' gittin' up."

But the night that I had an attack of appendicitis and needed some ice to pack my side when there was none nearer than Boothbay, Bubs was the first one there. He deposited the big bucket of chipped ice upon our front veranda and disappeared without a word. Next day Dad discovered that Bubs had taken the ice from the freezer that kept his ice cream at the store and that gallons had melted and had to be thrown away. But when Dad tried to pay Bubs for his spoiled ice cream, the old man was insulted.

"Guess I kin help out a neighbor, can't I?" he roared so fiercely that Dad only held out his hand and shook the other man's horny one in silent thanks. There weren't any words big enough, anyway, to say how he felt.

It annoyed Myrtie that while there was no church at Newagen to commandeer his services, Lee never refused an invitation to preach every year at the West Southport and Boothbay Harbor Methodist churches and even supplied at the Congregational Church at the Harbor. "But, Lee, you're supposed to be on vacation," she'd wail. "No one can keep going fifty-two Sundays in the year." But to Lee it was no chore to talk about his Lord.

Every Sunday night there was a "sing" at the Newagen school-house, led by a summer visitor with a splendid voice, where the young of both the native and summer people would go to sing lustily, "Throw out the lifeline across the dark wave!" or "Jesus, Saviour, pilot me," and other appropriately nautical hymns; and then hold hands as they walked home under the stars. The request for a more formal service of worship came to Lee from his friends the fishermen. One of them came shyly to the front porch of Snug-gery one evening to ask, "Mr. Nies, how did Jesus use to baptize his babies?"

"Come sit down," Lee offered, and his guest perched uneasily on the extreme edge of a canvas chair as Lee explained that differ-ent churches had differing ideas of how the baptism should be done; some felt the candidate should be covered *all over* with holy water as John the Baptist had baptized in the river; others felt *sprinkling water* upon the head was enough; while still others felt that the water should be *poured on* by the minister. There was a very old picture scratched upon a wall in ancient Rome which peo-ple said was supposed to be Jesus pouring water out of a shell to baptize a follower.

"I got a shell!" the fisherman broke in eagerly. "The prettiest shell you ever did see. I'd like my baby to be baptized the shell way. Would you do it, Mr. Nies? I don't want to go to no foreign church."

So it was arranged to have a baptism next Sunday morning at the little white schoolhouse; and when the word got around, the Newagen families eagerly asked that Mr. Nies "do their children, too." But it was Johnny Snowman who asked for "real" com-munion for the village.

"We ain't never had us a real Lord's Supper here to the Cape," he told Lee earnestly, shuffling his great sea boots uneasily. "I got some handsome birch over in my wood lot would make a pretty communion railin' for the schoolhouse. Want you should help me cut some?"

So Lee and Johnny took his crosscut saw and went out into

the wood lot to cut a communion rail; it was Johnny who suggested they keep on the bark, "it's so silverylike." Myrtie loaned them her best luncheon cloth to cover the teacher's desk for a communion table. With the big bunch of dahlias from someone's garden and the silvery railing, she thought this was the loveliest altar she'd ever seen; it belonged to the sea, to the sky, and to the fisher people.

That Saturday night before the service, Mrs. Kreuger arrived at the nearby Newagen Inn. Mrs. Kreuger was a lonely woman with a crown of silver hair whom Lee had comforted when her husband died recently and who had transferred her almost violent affections to Lee and his wife, Myrtie. Mrs. Kreuger's relatives had tried to get her to come to them, but she insisted upon following Lee around and appeared often when he preached. But this was the first time she had invaded their Newagen privacy. "I suppose we'll have to ask her here to dinner," Myrtie said dubiously, looking at the wobbly chairs and the table that had been a crate before it was covered with oilcloth. "I'll have lobster and hot biscuits."

But Mrs. Kreuger was enchanted by the whole setting of sea and rocks and melting biscuits. She was an extremely wealthy woman who could travel the world wherever she would, and so seldom wished to. "It's a real home like this, with children laughing and family love, that I miss," she told Lee wistfully. "I used to think my husband laughed too loud and scold him for it—but what I'd give now to hear him shout!"

What could they do but ask her to stay a few days—at the Inn, because they had no private bedroom, but to take her meals with them? So Mrs. Kreuger saw the first baptism and the first communion at the Newagen schoolhouse. "Will the fishermen really come?" Myrtie worried to Lee at breakfast. "They're so shy." But they trusted Lee. One by one, looking unfamiliar in their Sunday best, each man with a line of white around his sunburn where he'd got a haircut for the occasion, they came tiptoeing into the schoolhouse, walking as if the floor might heave like a deck under their feet at any moment. The women were stiffly starched too, and rustled as they wedged themselves into the little school seats, their awed eyes fixed upon the lady-birch communion railing. After Lee had baptized the babies, pouring the water upon their heads from the fisherman's handsome sea shell, he gave the invitation to the Lord's Supper.

"It makes no difference if you're a church member or not, or whether you've ever been inside a church before," Lee told his fishermen friends. His voice was so low you could hear behind it the eternal rote of the sea, God's organ sounding against the shore. "Jesus' first followers were fishermen too. If you love the Lord and want to follow His ways, you're invited. This is His table, free for everybody. Let him that is athirst for the water of life, come."

They flocked to the lady-birch altar and took their first communion while outside the open window the sea organ rolled and thundered, and the thrush sang his heart out in a solo of praise to Almighty God from the tip of a tall pine tree.

"It was the most wonderful service I ever saw," Mrs. Kreuger said later at dinner, with tears in her eyes. "Men, women, children, and little babies. The sea and the sky and the lady birch worshiped too. Lee, you should have a real church here. I'll build it!"

"No," cried Lee alarmed. "There are plenty of churches near here. Let Newagen worship as it likes! You can't force a natural surge toward God like this." Mrs. Kreuger was not convinced, but she went away next day looking thoughtful.

After that Lee was the fishermen's pastor at Newagen, though he had no salary and no church. The village people came to his little house instead. Evenings when it began to gray up they would come, silent as the other shadows on the mossy path, to The Snuggery to sit on the veranda with Lee, Myrtie, and us children. They would talk, strangely enough, about things of the spirit, often about problems at home that were troubling them. Lee never started the conversation this way; he let them go their own gait; but under the stars with the sea hushing down below on the shore, it is easy to tell what is deep in the heart. Often they only came to sing "Lead Kindly Light" or "Tell Me Why the Stars Do Shine." Several of the fishermen's wives had lovely voices. It was the only social life, besides the store, that the village afforded, and Lee was the only summer folk they accepted without reservation, as belonging to them.

With the gay insouciance of the man who knows little about boats and nothing much about engines, Lee had acquired cheaply a secondhand motorboat with a four-cylinder engine which rarely ran on more than two of them, and took his family adventuring among the islands. Summer storms can rise to almost hurricane heights along that rocky shore without warning, and one such mighty wind hit Lee's leaky boat one late afternoon as she emerged from the Kennebec River, coming home from Bath. As Lee headed out to sea, for he had to go around the point into Newagen Harbor, the waves grew frighteningly high and the boat, shuddering, stood on her beam-ends. Every time we'd go over a roller, she'd rise so high you could see her bottom, and then come down, crack! in the trough.

"Lee, are you sure we can make it?" Myrtie asked, her teeth chattering with fright.

"I don't know. If the engine keeps going we will," Lee told her. "Don't let the kids see you're scared. Sing something."

So we sang, shivering in the icy wind, wet to the skin, Myrtie leading while Ike and I came in loud on the chorus, and Lee prayed that the engine would keep coughing on. If it stopped for even a few moments, we'd all drown. But we all kept singing and the old engine kept chugging, and finally Lee was able to steer safely into the rock-sheltered little harbor at Newagen.

"There's an awful lot of people down on the fish pier," Myrtie said. "I wonder if anything's the matter? It's late, 'way after supper—why, they're all village people!"

As they climbed up the slippery ladder to the pier, the villagers said, "Evening, Mr. Nies," and melted away, but Lee managed to get hold of Johnny before he vanished up the bayberry path through the meadow. "What are you doing down here this time of night?" Lee demanded.

Johnny grinned sheepishly. "Yeastin' up some outside. We couldn't eat till we see you was home," he explained. "I was just about fixin' to go out after you, or to call the Coast Guard."

Being adopted by the village led to some queer experiences for Lee. "Git a chance and dodge up to see us some time," they'd say

Hen Marr read haltingly but in a voice that shook the veranda, his big finger following the words. "If we confess our sins, he is faithful and just to forgive us . . . to cleanse us from all unrighteousness. . . ."

"You have to do more than confess; you have to repent," Lee told him. "Do you repent?"

Cap'n Hen scratched his still handsome head, glanced over to where the kitchen curtain stirred as in a breeze, and sighed, hesitating. What pictures were going through his mind? Lee wondered. Sunrise in Haiti? Cool moonlight etching the Taj Mahal? More likely the garish lights of a hundred waterfront dives, cozy and warming to a man's gizzard after dark nights at sea. . . . The sounds and smell of the kingdoms of this world were drawn up before him in the rich mosaic of an old sailor's memory. Did he repent all that?

"Aye," he agreed finally, glancing toward the agitated curtain. "I do repent!"

"Then don't worry." Lee smiled suddenly at this man whose love for his wife was greater than his pride before his God. "You're forgiven."

"How can I be *sure?*" the captain gasped. "It can't be as easy as that!"

"Do *you* keep your word?" Lee demanded.

The old man bristled. "Anyone says I don't is a blankety—"

"All right," Lee interrupted hastily. "You read the promise. Just remember that God is a gentleman too!"

He strode off down the path, and next Sunday he grinned to himself to see big, old Cap'n Hen tramp down the tiny aisle at the schoolhouse after his shaky little wife. Lee hoped now that the two of them could be at peace for the little time that was left them to enjoy their little gray house together. But Mrs. Marr drew Lee aside after the meeting, her head wagging so in her agitation that he could hardly hear what she said.

"Hen's gittin' so good it scares me!" Maggie Marr worried. "He don't say anything worse 'n 'damn.' I'll thank you to quit prayin' for him. We been married nigh onto sixty years and I don't want him gettin' any further into heaven than I be. If you got to pray, pray us *equal*, Mr. Nies."

With a lump in his throat, Lee watched the two old lovers go off together down the dusty yellow road. Heaven wouldn't be heaven if her Hen who could swear in seven languages wasn't there; but Lee was sure that the Lord, who was a gentleman too, would understand, and make the proper arrangements.

CHAPTER 10

The Sahara of Boardinghouses

WHEN LEE LEFT the flourishing Stanton Avenue suburban church to try to unite two problem churches in Boston into one fruitful parish, Myrtie was upset. Radiant again with health, she expressed herself with vigor, protesting in the privacy of her and Lee's bedroom: When everything was going beautifully, why was Lee always dead set to move?

"But Myrtie, we've already stayed nine years, longer than any other pastor."

"You should think of the children," Myrtie went off on a new tack. "Susie has only one more year at high school. And what kind of children will Ike meet in Boston? All the little Slavinskis. . . ."

"My father knew only one word of English when he came here," Lee began sternly before his wife drew his lips down to her waiting ones, where their arguments ended as usual.

Lee's problem was that while Bromfield Street Church, situated in the heart of the business section of Boston, had money and few people, Tremont Street Church in the city's teeming South End had people and no money; its shifting, boardinghouse congregation couldn't begin to meet the expenses of the big half-empty church. The obvious solution was to sell the valuable property of Bromfield

Street in downtown Boston for enough to set up Tremont Street in the South End as a community social-service center. To do this sounded simple, but it wasn't, because the trustees of Bromfield Street would have none of it. This second oldest Methodist church in Boston had a fragment of Plymouth Rock in its cornerstone with the text, "Upon this rock I will build my church and the gates of hell shall not prevail against it." The trustees' decision not to sell Bromfield Street had been rock-firm until then. But the attendance had shrunk so much that twenty on a Sunday morning was a good congregation. The church was so well endowed, however, that the minister, the organist, and the sexton would still get their salaries even if no one came. The old-timers who hated change could go on kneeling cozily in cushioned pews while the plan to develop Tremont Street into a great Christian neighborhood center for the South End grew dusty in a pigeonhole. Lee was sent to Boston to merge the two churches if possible.

Tremont Street, a great stone Gothic church, had a proud history too, for it was here that the Women's Foreign Missionary Society of the Methodist Church was started by a handful of women, a movement that would lift up the condition of millions of women in nearly every country in the world. At the time of the society's inception, Tremont Street was in the middle of a fashionable neighborhood, a proud residential part of Boston. But as the parish families moved out into the suburbs, the church declined both in membership and in money for its upkeep; so that by the time Lee and Myrtie arrived, the church building was as run-down and shabby as the rest of the neighborhood. The faithful came to Sunday-morning services, but Sunday nights saw only a very few rattling about in the big church nave—while outside, the streets were teeming with lonesome, restless people.

"The Sahara of the South End," one newspaper article Lee showed Myrtie called the district, "a great wilderness of boarding-houses where 20,000 people could move out in twenty minutes . . . and frequently do."

"If only we could make Tremont Street into a church home for all those rootless people!" Lee explained to Myrtie, his eyes kindling. "People whose dreams haven't come true—kids from the country who wanted to sing in opera but who ended up behind a soda fountain instead; people who thought city streets were paved with gold and found them full of old dirty newspapers; students and young mothers who can't afford yet to move their babies out into country sunshine. We could—"

"Have a day nursery in the church vestry." Myrtie caught fire. "Have a place where the young can meet."

"Maybe a gymnasium like Stanton Avenue's to keep the teen-agers off the streets. . . ." Their plan blossomed luxuriously as they packed up to leave their pleasant white colonial parsonage to move to the South End of Boston into a solid brick block where several hundred other strangers lived also.

"Ichabod," Myrtie christened the parsonage the first time she stood, dismayed, before its front door with the peeling brown paint. The glory had certainly departed from the small square of mangy grass and weeds surrounded by the rusty iron fence. But that wasn't the worst hazard; every single shabby front door looked exactly like twenty others. "We'll have to count from the end of the block to see which hole in this—this rabbit warren is ours," she wailed. "Oh, Lee, even the leaves of those trees up there are greasy with old dirt I bet the Pilgrims left!"

Inside, Ichabod was even more appalling to anyone used to country light and air. The house ("slice of a spoiled raisin cake," Ike said) stood four stories high with only two or three rooms on a floor, connected by steep mountains of stairs and corridors so black you had to grope for the handrailing to keep from going headlong. The formerly magnificent front parlor had two narrow windows at one end revealing through grimy lace curtains the enormous dusty crystal chandelier, the gray-white marble fireplace that wouldn't burn, the acre or so of worn carpet. Beyond lay the vast dining room, also with windows at only one end, whose only connection with food was a contraption more "dumb" than "waiter" which worked only seldom and then protestingly. The kitchen down in the basement had a brick floor icy to the feet on a winter's morning and a black iron gas stove that popped and crackled alarmingly.

"If I had five servants I *might* be able to keep this place clean!"

Myrtie moaned after she ran down three flights of stairs because Lee had forgotten his key. But when Lee suggested he leave the door unlocked while he went on another errand, Myrtie was firm. "No you don't! You know who I found in our front vestibule when I went to take in the milk this morning? A drunk! He called me 'sweetie!' "

"For the love of Pete," Lee gasped. "Why didn't you call me?"

"Interrupt your sermon?" Myrtie protested. "I just picked him up by the back of the collar and dumped him in the next doorway! It might be his. How do I know what kind of a—a barroom you've brought us to, Lee Nies!" She giggled suddenly, snorted "sweetie!" and fled back upstairs to where she was making beds.

Lee called upon everyone in his block during his first week on the street. He looked so little like most people's idea of a minister when he rang the doorbell and stood there in his blue suit that was always comfortably rumpled, his jauntily cocked gray hat, and his easy smile that he insisted he had to say, "Look, no brushes to sell!" before he was allowed inside. But ten minutes after he'd met them, most of the boardinghouse inhabitants were eagerly confiding their life secrets; they knew instinctively that they could trust him and they were starved for company.

"They've fed you so much tea and cakes I'll have to put you on a diet," Myrtie moaned, regarding Lee's bulging waistline.

Every creed, age, and nationality, Lee found, lived under these cracked, high ceilings—Mormons, Roman Catholics, Protestants of every denomination, spiritualists who offered to lift a table for him with "See, no hands"; and Chinese, Russians, Turks, and other plain Americans with family roots in Europe. "The ones I'm sorriest for are the old women," Lee told Myrtie. "They cling to a precarious existence in these dull, dark rooms as a cat walks a high fence, fearful of falling off into a sickness that would wipe out their savings—Lord love 'em. He does, but they aren't sure about it. If only they could learn, *really* learn, that there's nothing to be afraid of. Maybe if they'll come to church, the hymns or the music will teach them, if I can't."

Lee preached first at Bromfield Street Church, later at Tremont Street. In the former the music was excellent, the handful of worshipers well-dressed and pleasantly prosperous. But the big shabby auditorium of Tremont Street needed many things; there must be some way to get enough people coming to church to pay for fixing this place up, Lee worried. The organ squeaked and a few stops were useless; the brown stains on the walls showed where the roof leaked. How was he going to fill that big auditorium—make the church really a home for the lonely who swarmed about but never inside it? Then one night at dinner the answer was handed to him, as he jokingly said later to Myrtie, "on a platter, at least, in a cup of consommé!"

Wilbur Hascall, a noted Boston composer, sat next to Lee at the table and spent the entire soup course bewailing the lack of musical taste of the average Protestant churchgoer who preferred "Brighten the Corner Where You Are" to Bach and Mozart. When Protestantism had abandoned the mass, he insisted, it had unhappily substituted a passion for bastard hymns for Gregorian chants and real music. Methodists especially delighted in musical mediocrity.

"I'm not so sure of that," Lee retorted. "If they heard great church music, adequately played. . . ." His eyes lighted. "Why don't you come down to our church and try it out? If you'll be our organist, I can't pay you a tithe of what you're worth, but I can guarantee you can play anything you like. My hunch is classical music can be made as popular as jazz."

Hascall was excited. "I'll try it for six months," he agreed. "After all, my father wrote hymns." He chortled. "Me, a musical missionary to the South End! That is, if you really mean it?"

"You just got yourself a job, feller," Lee twinkled.

"Boston Composer's Night," the black print shouted on the cards with which Lee flooded the neighborhood. "No admission charge. Hear the magnificent chorales of Bach. Wilbur Hascall, fellow of the American Guild of Organists, will play one of his own compositions." The first Sunday night the big auditorium was half full; but by the third Sunday, there was standing room only. Hascall invited other friends of his to come as "guest composers," and the untutored public loved it. There was something about the great organ music, rolling out from under a master's fingers, that spoke to tired, lonely people in a language that drew them out of the dusty city streets to a cool mountain peak where, like Enoch, you would walk with God.

"I don't know what it says, but it's bigger than me," Lee heard one shopgirl say as she went out of the church. "I never knew before that high-brow music really made sense!"

As Hascall taught the young people's choir to sing Bach chorales, their number grew till there were hardly seats enough in the choir loft. Students from the nearby Boston universities and schools flocked for the privilege of studying church music under Hascall. After the service, over cocoa and cookies, the young people met their neighbors they'd passed shyly on the brick sidewalks. As the congregations grew, the church finances picked up and the whole hive of the church began to hum with activity.

Lee himself went often to listen to Hascall practice, sitting alone and entranced in the empty church nave while the organ music rolled magnificently about him, lifting him up to that vast, shining place where there is neither time nor circumstance, merely "something bigger than me." Once Hascall surprised Lee jotting down notes of music upon the back of an old envelope, took it from him, and played the melody through on his organ.

"Why, Lee, that's good!" Hascall gasped. "And you say you never had any musical education? Extraordinary!" The notes were a setting for "Unfold, Ye Portals Everlasting" which Lee had been playing to himself for years upon his old upright piano. "I'll orchestrate this and we'll have the choir sing it next Sunday," Hascall promised, beaming.

Lee had been writing music secretly ever since he'd hummed his own sleepy lullabies for Ike and me, but it had never occurred to him his tunes had any merit. But next Sunday morning shook him. As he listened to the organ soaring up and up as he had told it to, as he heard the choir of two hundred young voices singing the grand old words as he, Lee Nies, had showed them how, he wished suddenly and inexplicably that his father were here to hear it, too.

"To be free to choose and to choose God's way is all that makes us different from the animals," George Nies had told his small son in his shoeshop. Lee felt that his father would be glad he had decided to be a minister instead of trying to be President of the United States. Lee hadn't been sure before, but now he knew. Queer how music said the unsayable. Was it perhaps the language of heaven, now but dimly understood?

But all honeymoons come to an end, and so did that of composer Hascall and Tremont Street Church.

"Sooner or later, you always have trouble with the choir," Myrtie sighed wisely when Lee told her that Hascall had threatened to leave before his six months were up because his young people's choir wanted to sing classical church music on Sunday mornings only but had asked for a song service of popular hymns on Sunday evenings. "Something with some pep," as one boy protested. Myrtie mused, "It must be the artistic temperament or something. Or maybe musicians just crave excitement?"

> *"Two men looked through prison bars,*
> *One saw mud and the other saw stars."*

Lee quoted, smiling crookedly.

"Wilbur lives in such a rarefied atmosphere musically, he can't figure that earth is good for anything, even to plant in. I'll have to have a talk with him tonight after church. Make a twelve-egg angel cake, will you, sugar?" They grinned to each other; it was this true, tried recipe that had worked on the Presiding Elder and many times since, chiefly because they knew it would.

After service, Hascall stormed into Ichabod, flung his briefcase of music on the top of Myrtie's battered-from-many-movings old upright piano. "I'm through!" he shouted to Lee. "I resign as of this instant! What horror did we sing tonight? 'Jesus, Lover of My Soul' to the bastard tune of 'Juanita.' I tell you, Lee, it's *sacrilege.*"

"Yes, yes. It was pretty bad," Lee admitted, gently pushing the composer into the easy chair. His glance added to Myrtie, "Bring some angel cake and coffee, quick!" As Lee fed the weary musician, he turned upon him the full battery of his Texas charm. "You're worn out, and I don't wonder. You've been doing a magnificent job, Wilbur. We didn't even have standing room in the church tonight. And how they did sing 'Faith of our Fathers, living still . . .' Some of the greatest sermons have been written in hymns."

Lee got up, went over to the old upright, and slid his searching fingers over the keys, oblivious that Wilbur was a noted composer and he, Lee, had never had a music lesson in his life; he knew only how to speak through his fingers what was in his heart. The music flowed softly from one great hymn to another till finally Lee drifted into a melody that made Hascall straighten in his chair. Lee talked dreamily as he played on.

"Once there was a good man who wrote a song," Lee murmured to the music. "It wasn't a great song, musically, but it made people feel happier, live more bravely when they sang the words. They weren't even great poetry; but they made folks remember that life isn't all poverty, and getting sick, and paying the bills; beyond there lies eternity and the Great White Throne." Hascall listened, frozen, as Lee flung back his head. "It was a good song and a good man. Listen, my friend."

Lee's golden tenor filled the long, dim, shabby room.

> *"Oh come, angel band,*
> *Come and around me stand;*
> *Bear me away on your snowy wings*
> *To my immortal home. . . ."*

"Stop! Stop it, Lee Nies!" Hascall had jumped to his feet, had come to grip Lee's shoulder, and there were tears running down the musician's cheeks. *"My father wrote that hymn.* Darn you, Lee. I knew you'd get around me. I'll play your damn organ till hell freezes over!"

Another profane but greathearted man who helped Lee in his ministry in the great Sahara of boardinghouses was Dr. K. He was a physician so successful that he got little sleep nights, but when Lee found a sick man who couldn't afford a doctor but who shrank from the stark charity of a big hospital, Lee would ring up his friend. "Another of your blankety-blank lame ducks!" Dr. K. would rage. "How in the blank blank do you expect me to make a living?" Then he would rush over, tend the sick man gently, likely as not buy the needed medicines out of his own pocket. These three men, outwardly so different and inwardly so alike in being attuned to human need, loved each other inarticulately and wove a ministry of music, medicine, and kindness that warmed the whole neighborhood.

As usual, Lee made friends with everyone he met, even in the back alley behind Ichabod. The ashman who carried away the cans was careful not to bang the barrels on Monday morning when the minister might be "sleeping off his sermon" of yesterday; the chief of the Boston police whom Lee met socially gave him a "courtesy card" which he called laughingly "my-park-by-the-hydrant ticket"; and Big Mike, the cop assigned to control traffic in front of the Tremont Street Church, worried over the way Lee was apt to linger in his church study after the evening service, talking to anyone from the congregation who had a problem in his heart.

"It ain't safe, Father," Mike warned anxiously. "You all alone here with some o' them dope heads. You don't know 'em like I do."

"But I'm not alone, Mike," Lee told him. He drew the big policeman to the door of the church nave. The lights there were out, so the street lamp from outside shone through the tall stained-glass windows making a dim radiance in the quiet church that seemed to hover over the pews. "The Shekinah," Lee murmured, remembering his Hebrew. "It shone so brightly before the Ark that the priests could not see, Mike. . . . 'The glory of the Lord filled the house of the Lord.' " Mike's eyes were awed and a little frightened as he muttered, well, maybe he'd better be going. Lee patted the big policeman's arm affectionately, adding, "And I have you, Mike."

Lee never told Myrtie how desperate were some of the characters with whom he talked in his lonely church, unless he needed her help with them. One Sunday evening after Lee had preached on "The Good Life," a young man of twenty-five came to his study to see him. "None of us can avoid evil thoughts entirely any more than we can keep the crows from flying over our heads," Lee had admitted honestly. "But we can keep them from building nests in our hair!"

"I guess I got plenty of nests in my hair, Mr. Nies," the other man told him. He squirmed uneasily under Lee's clear, quiet, blue gaze; finally he blurted out, "I've got one of the neatest extortion setups in this town! And I've had 'customers' within two blocks of this church!"

Lee felt as if a cold wind had blown over him but he said, quietly still, "I don't doubt it." And waited again. Sometimes the only way to get the evil out of your system was to vomit it out.

The man in the study chair was sweating. He cried out suddenly and buried his face in his hands as he sobbed, "I wasn't always this way. I was brought up in a Christian home. You got to help me out of this mess!"

"Pray, 'Oh God, help me!'" Lee ordered sternly.

When the wretched man obeyed, Lee ordered, "Louder! And mean it!"

"*Oh God, help me!*" The younger man cried so bitterly loud that Mike, the cop, appeared in the open study doorway and his face grew angry as he saw who Lee's visitor was. He sputtered, "Father Nies, you don't know. . . ." Lee motioned him away so imperiously that Mike retreated as far as the front door.

"But the devil came out of him with that loud cry," Lee explained to Mike later, and the Irishman crossed himself quickly. Queer things were going on in this heretic church where the minister talked about the glory of Hebrew gods. As the Reverend himself said, the good Lord had publicans and sinners as his friends, but things like that didn't work in the South End of Boston. Or did they?

This man who'd cried for the help of God and found it, had a girl who had borne him a child who was already three months old. Lee married his new parishoner to the mother, who held the baby in her arms and marveled at what was happening to her. She was only twenty but already life had taught her to expect nothing good. Now she had suddenly acquired a husband and respectability. "My wife will call on you," Lee promised as he handed her her wedding lines.

Myrtie called, invited the girl to the Ladies' Aid and enrolled the baby in the Cradle Roll as a matter of course; she also gave one of the other streetwalkers work in her kitchen until Lee could find her a real job. But Myrtie was careful to see that her new maid left each afternoon before her young son Ike came home from high school. It wasn't that she didn't trust the Lord to take care of Ike or believe in the girl's change in attitude. "Thou shalt not tempt the Lord thy God," Myrtie explained. "You know, Lee, one of the things I like best about the Bible is its common sense!"

One of the worst problems they had to fight in the South End was Lee's giving all his salary away before the family had its innings. Though his pay check here was much larger than at Stanton Avenue, there was never any residue. Every professional "deadbeat" in Boston read the gilt-lettered sign in front of the church on Tremont Street giving Lee's address as pastor, and came to try him out. Lee was always certain he could detect when a faker was shamming, and Myrtie was equally certain that he could not. Which led to one of the few bitter quarrels the two had ever had.

"Lee, you didn't give that frowsty-looking man any *cash*, did you?" Myrtie worried one morning as the front door closed behind an especially seedy individual who looked as if he had slept in his clothes. Lee couldn't give away any more money because he *knew* she had to have a new dress to wear for Social Union next Monday night when she and Lee were to sit at the head table, up on the platform.

"I merely *loaned* him forty dollars to pay his way back home to Cleveland," Lee murmured, avoiding Myrtie's accusing eyes. "He's a leather salesman who came here for a convention and—er—celebrated too well. He got—er—'rolled' is, I believe, the expression, and woke up this morning in a strange room, without a cent. He's a Methodist, so naturally when he saw our sign. . . ."

"And you fell for that—that guff?" Myrtie could contain her wrath no longer, her breath coming fast, her cheeks blazing. "You *know* he'll never send the money back! *You gave that bum my dress for Social Union.*"

Lee stared at her unhappily. Myrtie seldom got really angry but when she did. . . . Social Union when all the leading Methodists got together for a banquet was a big event in her life and he *had* promised her. . . .

"I'm going right downtown and *charge* me a new dress at Jordan's!" Myrtie's tone warned Lee not to try to stop her.

"Charge accounts" were financial lifesavers which Myrtie had discovered since coming to Boston, and of which Lee disapproved sharply. For the eighteen years Myrtie had been a minister's wife, she had always been pinched for money; so when she found out that all you had to do to buy something you couldn't afford was to say grandly, "Charge it, please," her relief knew no bounds. That the bills had to be paid at the end of the month was no problem; you simply sent them a check out of the new joint account Lee had opened at the bank. Checks to Myrtie were not real money; they were merely counters in the game of financial checkers you played with the bank, trying to keep one square ahead. She was always surprised when a check "bounced" as it frequently did and Lee had to cover it at the bank.

No more was said about the Social Union dress, but two days later Myrtie came pirouetting gaily into his study. "Don't I look nice?" The dark-blue chiffon dress she wore was the color of her eyes and foamed about her in soft, lovely waves; she looked more than nice; she was gorgeous, and knew it, with the frank innocence of a child showing off new shoes.

Lee kissed her. "But, dear, how much—"

She pressed her fingers against his lips. "Oh, Lee, I have so many years to make up for! All that time in bed. . . ." She slid him a glance from under long eyelashes. "When your Cleveland bum sends back the forty dollars. . . ."

"You'd better run along. I'm busy," Lee told her, coldly.

By the end of the week, there was still no letter from Cleveland and an armed neutrality between Myrtie and Lee made our breakfast table a place to exit from hastily. It was frightening to see our parents look across the sugar and cream with hostility, for it had never happened before. As I came in from high school that afternoon, the sound of raised voices held me paralyzed at the front door. "You're overdrawn at the bank again," Lee was saying icily. "It's that dress. I shall close out the joint bank account and the charge accounts at the store too. We simply can't go on this way, spending more money than we have. I tell you, it's criminal."

"There would have been enough in the bank if you didn't give away every cent!" Myrtie flared back. "If you didn't think more of a bum than of your own wife. . . ."

A letter slid through the mail slot at my frozen feet and I picked it up automatically. Then I began to run up to the study, shouting, "It's from Cleveland! Open it, quick!" I stood there, breathless, watching Myrtie go red and white, twist her fingers into a nervous pattern, while Lee read the letter. Slowly he handed her the blue slip that fell out.

"It's for a hundred dollars! Oh, Lee!" Myrtie flung herself, laughing and crying, into his arms and his cheek was against her wet one and there was something in her eyes that made me tiptoe away to my own room and close the door. But not before I heard her cry, "Now I can have the hat to go with my blue dress! I saw one I wanted so badly it made me *hurt*."

Lee rested his cheek against her soft hair. She'd never grow up. But what did money matter when you'd loved her since she was seven? When she'd scrubbed five parsonages and borne your children? She'd be the prettiest girl up there on the platform at Social Union and she'd be yours. What if she couldn't do arithmetic? Myrtie was magnificent. "Get the hat, sweet," Lee surrendered.

That spring the bishop and church conference authorities decided, as they had every right to do under Methodist church law, to unite Bromfield Street and Tremont Street churches with a new joint board of trustees. Bromfield Church was sold for $400,000. The original trustees of Bromfield Street felt they should control this fund, rather than the new joint board, so they promptly sued in the civil courts the bishop, the district superintendent (as the Presiding Elder was now called), Lee as resident pastor, and the other newly appointed trustees of the fund. Thus all proceeds from the sale of Bromfield Street Church were so tied up indefinitely as to be of no practical value in developing the big shabby Tremont Street Church for which Lee and Myrtie had hoped so much. All their dreams for a great social center in the South End of Boston had gone aglimmering.

Lee's sense of failure was further increased by his experience with his Human Fly.

Lee smelled him before he saw the little man standing there in the open study door; he was red-haired, wiry, and he hadn't shaved for days. Obviously he had come straight across the street to the church from the saloon bar. He swayed as he announced portentously, "I'm the Human Fly. Do you think God would really hear me, if I—prayed?" He accused, "You *said* He would listen. You said so, mister, tonight. I heard you through the church window!"

"He might if you threw that gin bottle into my wastepaper basket," Lee told him. As the little man obeyed, his hand trembling, Lee asked curiously, "What did you mean—Human Fly?"

The little man straightened his shoulders. "*I* didn't say so. The newspaper called me that. When I painted William Penn's hat in Philadelphia. I painted the Boston State House dome, too. And flagpoles nobody else'll climb. When my hand don't shake." He held out his hand, regarded its trembling, shoved it back into his ragged pocket to pull out a rosary. "My mother gave me that. She told me when I wanted to do something bad to look at this and it'd stop me. It has, too. But nowadays my hand shakes so—" his voice rose in a frightened crescendo— "I can't paint no more. If you don't help me off the booze, I'm done for!"

"I can't help you, but the Lord can," Lee told him. "Let's ask Him."

When they finally got up from their knees, the little Human Fly was sober enough to tell his pitiful story. "My own mother died when I was seven. After the funeral, my father, the drunken bum, told me he hadn't been married to her anyway, and now he was going to live with his real wife who didn't want brats like me. I looked after myself from then on. Nobody was goin' to get me in no orphan's home! I sold newspapers. Nights I slept anywhere it was warm, over the subway grating, in a big pipe where they was fixin' the street. Some nights it was so cold, I'd have to push away the snow to get out of the pipe. I never slept in a real room again till I was twenty and then I liked to smothered to death!"

One day the newsboy had stopped by Park Street Church to watch a man high up painting the steeple. When he finally came down, the street urchin had asked, "Hey, mister, you git paid good for that?" "Plenty, kid. But watch your step," the man grinned. So the lad had tried being a steeplejack; he found he had a good head for heights and a steady hand and made more in a day than he had formerly in a month. The little redheaded man told Lee proudly, "I'm good, I am. They wouldn't call me the 'Human Fly' right out in print, if I wasn't, would they, mister?"

"Of course you're good." Lee patted his shoulder, glanced at his watch. "It's after midnight. Why don't you come home with me?"

Lee laid a mattress upon the brick kitchen floor so that the little Human Fly wouldn't feel smothered in a small bedroom and the next morning Myrtie cooked the little man a good breakfast. "Before you try for another job, you need decent clothes," Lee said. He called up a friend who worked in a cut-rate store and sent the Human Fly down there. He came back, radiant, to the parsonage, wearing a new outfit from the skin out. He was a different man in the new gray suit, the necktie, unbroken shoes. He shot out the clean white cuffs of his shirt from his coat sleeves triumphantly. "I didn't think you were on the level last night when you said to seek first the kingdom of heaven and all these things would be added to me," he told Lee. "Cripes, it's true! But I never thought the Lord God would add me *cuffs!*"

Once off liquor, the Human Fly—he refused to tell his real name, if indeed he remembered it—began to earn good money again, for his profession was hardly a crowded one. Sometimes Lee went to watch the little man work, craning his neck to see the Fly wave down from his high perch upon a roof peak. And every night the Human Fly would ring the parsonage front doorbell, hand Lee every cent he had earned except what he needed for next day's food and lodging, and go away again. Lee started an account in the savings bank for him.

Then one night he didn't come. Uneasy, Lee waited up for him until two in the morning, but it was almost daylight before the doorbell finally rang. There stood the Human Fly, his hands trembling again, his new clothes filthy; he was weeping drunk. "They spiked it, mister!" he cried, grabbing at Lee's dressing gown. "They spiked the lemonade on me. I guess you don't want me to come in here. I ain't no good. But I *said*, 'I don't want no drink, just some lemonade. . . .' "

"We'll make some hot coffee." Lee steadied the weeping little man and pulled him inside. For the rest of the night he and the Human Fly drank coffee and talked earnestly, and in the morning the depressed little man went away, sober, cleaned up, presumably to his job. But he never came back. Lee looked for him all over Boston, getting Mike and the other cops to help him, but it was no use; the little Fly had gone back into the dark ooze of the big city from whence he had emerged.

"I failed him," Lee worried.

"You gave him something clean for a few days anyway," Myrtie comforted him. "Like his mother gave him the rosary he kept. What you did for him isn't lost. He'll remember it wherever he goes. He's weak, that's all."

But Lee, dejected, couldn't shake off the conviction that in the Human Fly's failure he too had failed again. He preached the next Sunday on "Am I my brother's keeper?" and coming from a full and humble heart, his words brought to the congregation an electric stillness louder than shouts. But Myrtie, tense in her pew, wished Lee wouldn't take things so hard.

"Sin is not merely a personal aberration," Lee told his people. "We live in each other. In every crooked politician we allow to be elected, we sin a little. In every criminal who walks the streets of Boston, we see a child we did not help while there was still time. In the squalor and poverty of this great city, we see our own children defiled! We *are* our brother's keeper, and the sins of omission and commission tar us both."

As he stood up there in his great carved pulpit, mourning his Human Fly, Myrtie's heart swelled with love of him. Yet, strangely, she was a little afraid of him, too, for this was the stern priest, not her loving husband, who spoke. He seemed suddenly worlds away from her, in a far shining place where she could not go. "Oh Lord," she prayed, "take care of him. I know you love him like I do." It seemed to her that when Lee came down from his pulpit that morning his face shone as Moses' had when he'd talked with God.

At long last the Tremont Street official board decided to sell Ichabod, which was plainly a "parson's wife-killer," and move the minister's family into a big elevator apartment on Huntington Avenue. "Everything all on one floor! Plenty of windows for light and sun!" Myrtie caroled as she flitted happily from room to room. "And the children can walk to the Public Library if they have to look up anything for school. Did Susie tell you, Lee, she was going to be Nerissa in the high-school *Merchant of Venice?*"

"Yes." Lee looked at Myrtie a trifle nervously, confessing, "I did something today. I bought the kids tickets to see *Macbeth* next Saturday night. I thought with Sothern and Marlowe playing, it'd really be educational. . . ."

"Oh, Lee, *I'm glad!*" Myrtie raised her small chin defiantly. Even if some Methodists did think the stage immoral, she'd never been able to see much difference between Lee's reading the plays so constantly, the children's studying them and acting Shakespeare at school, and their going to see a professional production, complete with footlights and costumes. Lee lost himself in the music of the words in Shakespeare plays as he did in other music. It was a family joke that once when Lee had been sitting up late in the living room of Ichabod, rereading *Macbeth*, he'd looked up to see a housebreaker just creeping up the stairs from the kitchen with a gun in his hand. Lee stared at the intruder absently over his reading glasses, and still lost in the great *Macbeth*, roared in his best Elizabethan, "*Get thee gone, villain!*" The thief, terrified, got himself gone, and Lee went back to his reading, without even getting up. Anyone who tried to find something to steal in a parsonage was a fool, anyway.

Ike and I were too excited to eat dinner on the night of the play; it didn't seem possible we were actually going to see a *real* theater, not just Johnny dressed in his mother's tunic, squeaking did he see a dagger? We arrived at the theater before it opened, blew ourselves to an enormous banana split, and then, feeling vaguely uncomfortable, mounted the endless stairs to the front row of the "peanut gallery." They were wonderful seats; we could lean over the red-velvet railing and look right down upon Macbeth's dark head and Lady Macbeth's trailing draperies. To these two children of the Puritan parsonage, no scenery was necessary, for the scene was already painted upon our wild imaginings and the voice of Macbeth might have been drawn from our own shaking breasts, we knew so well what he must say. We followed every word, every gesture, our tension mounting almost unbearably as Macbeth began his famous soliloquy.

> *"Is this a dagger that I see before me*
> *The handle toward my hand?"*

As the great actor paused for effect, Ike and I, rushing mentally through the so-familiar speech, thought, agonized, that he must have forgotten, so we prompted loudly from the peanut gallery, "Come, let me clutch thee!" Only to collapse in hot shame into our red plush seats as the outraged people on either side of us, hissed us to silence. It was a memorable evening on both sides of the footlights, the first time the preacher's kids attended the theater.

When I entered Boston University that fall as a very green freshman, partly because the College of Liberal Arts was just down the street from our new apartment and partly because preacher's kids were granted scholarships there, Mrs. Kreuger celebrated the occasion by asking us all to dinner at the nearby luxurious hotel where she lived. Her living room with its red wallpaper, gilt furniture that looked like gold, her library and bedroom where she and her sister-in-law who kept her company slept, were the most sumptuous apartment I had ever seen. It looked much more stagy than the Shakespeare play had. And the dinner down in the big dining room with its snowy tablecloth, shining silver, and endless courses slid in front of you by waiters determined to stuff you like a Thanksgiving turkey would have served us at the parsonage for a week.

"Come often, children," Mrs. Kreuger urged, patting my hand as we left. "We're neighbors now. And I'm a lonely old woman."

How could anyone be lonely with the lobby bursting with other grand ladies who looked just like her? I wondered. Expensive black dresses, crowns of silver hair, black velvet ribbons around their sagging necks . . . where had I seen them before? Why, they were the same ladies who always filled the front seats at Boston Symphony afternoon concerts, where Dad and I went when parishioners gave us their season tickets they weren't using! These crowned Boston ladies had had the same seats for fifty years and so sanctified them. Most of them must live here at the hotel, I decided, looking about the lobby with awe.

"If Catherine Kreuger had been brought up when a lady could work, with all her energy she could have headed a vast industry," Dad said as we walked back home through the brightly lighted streets (no more stumbling over uprooted bricks to hunt for Ichabod's front door). "I wish we could find her something to do."

But Mrs. Kreuger found her own job. She bustled into our apartment one spring day while the whole family were tearing about, trying to help Myrtie find four pairs of whole socks for Lee to take to Minneapolis. He had been elected delegate to go to the Methodist General Conference, there to "represent the whole of New England," Myrtie had told us kids impressively. "He's very young for such an honor! People from all over the world will be there, black, white, yellow Methodists, and your father, too!" She looked up at Lee proudly, announcing, "Someday he'll preside over General Conference as bishop!"

"Now, Myrtie," Lee had chided. "She's just a little bit prejudiced, kids."

We were all so excited it was small wonder that Mrs. Kreuger's offer was almost an anticlimax. "I've been looking up the land you own in Newagen, Lee," she told him impressively. "There's plenty of room for another cottage. I'm going to build a bigger one than Snuggery there, where you can hold meetings for all the Newagen fishermen! If you won't let me build a church, you should at least have a veranda big enough for all of them to sit on when they come to tell you their troubles." She hesitated and added, almost shyly for her, "Would you mind if I added a small apartment for me and my sister-in-law too? So we could be part of a real family a few days in the year?"

"We'd love having you!" the warmhearted Myrtie cried, throwing her arms impetuously about the older woman, trying to imagine a life empty of Lee and the children. When Lee said nothing, just stood there frowning, tears came into Mrs. Kreuger's eyes. "You don't want me!" she choked.

"Of course we want you." Lee patted her shoulder, but he still hesitated. "Why don't you build you a house and we'll still live in Snuggery next door where we belong? I'll gladly give you the land. But I hardly think . . ."

"Oh Lee, don't be such a kill-joy!" Myrtie cried. "She's building the house big for *Newagen,* not for us. You can't blame anyone for wanting to be part of a *family*." So it was settled that the building at Newagen should begin while Lee was away at General Conference.

But Lee did not seem as excited about going as Myrtie was. "If you should happen to see my Human Fly at church, you keep him. Bring him home here till I get back, hear?" he begged Myrtie.

Couldn't he ever forget the queer little man? Why should Lee feel forever that the failure was his? Myrtie demanded, privately sure she'd never keep the smelly little Fly in her new apartment.

"But I *have* failed," Lee told her, quietly. "Not only with him. Bromfield and Tremont Street may not be able to work as a united church for years. Not till they have a man as pastor they aren't suing in the courts, anyway. How the fellows ever came to elect me as delegate to General Conference. . . ."

"Because they *like* you! How could that mess possibly be your fault?" Myrtie asked hotly. "The trustees decided to sell Bromfield Street. You just happened to be the minister." Her eyes widened as she realized what he was implying. "Lee Nies, are you trying to tell me we have to move again—*so soon?*"

Lee nodded, unhappily. "I just had a talk with the bishop. He says that at least church union is a step in the right direction, no matter what the courts decide about the money." He looked questioningly at his wife. "Myrtie, we've been offered Trinity in Worcester. You better begin packing, sugar."

Myrtie shivered. All those packing boxes again after they'd been in this beautiful apartment only a year; the piano legs to wrap in comforters; a new parsonage to settle where none of the draperies would ever fit. Suddenly her face brightened as she remembered, "But Lee, Trinity is one of the biggest churches in the Conference!"

Lee nodded. "Yes, I guess so. It's another big chance. I hope I don't flub it. I wish I'd had time to pack my books; you'll have to manage." He looked around him for the last time at his Tremont Street study. There were some things even as good a wife as Myrtie could not pack for him; the splinters of his shattered dreams for the great South End church center, the sure salvation of his Human Fly.

CHAPTER 11

Mountain Peaks in Everyday Living

"Few people can live very long on the mountain peaks of spiritual communion with God," Lee often said, somewhat ruefully. "They have to come down into the valley again as Moses did. The important thing is, after every tumble, to keep climbing back up."

Lee was to have more mountain peaks of his own at the Trinity Church, Worcester, than ever before and to spend there some of the happiest days of his mature manhood. Worcester, in the spring of 1914 when he arrived there, was still at heart a big, sprawling country town which was growing too fast for its britches. Its great factories were to grow still more vast as the war emergency made itself felt, and many of the workers were second generation from Europe as Lee himself was, simple, friendly people who still believed that "In God we trust" was the backbone of Christian democracy.

In this congenial atmosphere Lee was like the ugly duckling spreading his surprised snowy wings, exultant and rejoicing in each new sun. He called upon every one of his thousand church members during the first half year after he arrived; also as he rattled about in his old Dodge, if he saw a new house a-building, he would slam on his car brakes.

"I came to welcome you to your new church home!" he would beam at the homeowner watching his new house go up. "I'm from Trinity. Could I see your place?" By the time he and the householder wobbled back down the plank that did service for front steps they were firm friends. What was more impressive to newcomers, Lee never forgot a name or a face, but would greet each newcomer correctly when he shook hands at the church door after service. By the end of a year of such neighborliness, over four hundred new names had been added to Trinity's already large roster of families; and several of the church officials were disgruntled when they arrived late for Sunday-morning service to find their pews already filled.

But Lee would not be satisfied until the evening service was equally crowded. He liked this big ugly red-brick church with its typically American congregation where mill owners shared their hymnbooks with their hired help. Democracy had a language he understood, and which he felt the church was best fitted to interpret. But his informality offended some of the more conservative.

"I'll never go to your 'Warm Up the Heart' Sunday-night shindigs!" one official member snorted angrily to Lee. "Might as well go to the movies!"

But Lee's musical Sunday evenings were soon so popular that the ushers were packing 1500 worshipers, mostly young people, into the downstairs pews and up in the wide balcony; while the overflow stood up in the back of the church so they could better watch the screen that slid down in front of the pulpit for the opening song service. The words of the hymns were thrown, greatly magnified, upon the screen, while Lee himself led the singing, assisted by a vested choir of over fifty voices.

"Let's all sing this next one together like we used to when we were in the front parlor, with Mom playing the piano and Pop not too sure of the bass!" Lee's friendly smile as he stood there would cement the restless crowd into one common church family. He would nod at the organist, then his golden tenor would ring out, joined instantly by the soaring choir:

"I will sing you a song of a faraway land,
Of a country beyond the blue sea;
Where beneath the blue skies
Jesus suffered and died. . . .
Where he suffered for you and for me."

Often he would pick out a volunteer from the congregation, and ask him to sing the next verse alone. "Come up here, Linda!" he called to one little girl whose flutelike piping he'd noticed on the high notes. "Let's you and I sing this piece together. It's a Christmas song, so I'm sure you know it. But why should we sing it only one day in the year, when the Christ child is born every day in someone's heart?" Linda was so small Lee lifted her up in his arms so that her voice could be heard in the back of the big church. Together they began:

"Away in a manger, no crib for his bed,
The little Lord Jesus laid down his sweet head . . ."

Linda's voice was as clear and true, almost as strong as an adult's. Lee gradually began to hum, then stopped entirely. But Linda sang on with the organ, a silver flute dropping shining notes into the darkness of the auditorium where the quiet people heard, breathless, the wonderful, gentle, lullaby of another baby in Bethlehem, the One Altogether Lovely.

"The cattle are lowing, the baby awakes,
But little Lord Jesus no crying he makes;
I love thee, Lord Jesus! Look down from the sky,
And stay by my bed until morning is nigh."

The hush of perfect tribute to beauty followed the little girl's song; but when the lights flashed on, she had her arms around Lee's neck with her face turned away, a little frightened at what she had done. Lee set her down gently. "Keep singing, Linda," he told her. "Someday the whole world will hear your song!" He had no way of knowing that he had started an opera singer upon the long hard climb to success. But he did smile to himself to spy down in the front pew the official who'd said he'd never attend these "Sunday-night shindigs" taking off his glasses to wipe his eyes.

Children were more important to Lee than adults, because "the shape of things to come" was in their hands. He always gave a fifteen-minute Sunday-morning sermon for them, illustrated by real "texts" they could handle after church. "Bear and Forbear" were Ike's Swiss bear, which nodded its head when touched, and my old Punk, the hairless Teddy bear which every child recognized at once as beloved. For his "Bread of Life" sermon, Lee used as texts four loaves of bread apparently uncut; but inside one loaf was a pack of playing cards; inside another, a mirror; and buried in another loaf was a dollar bill. Lee would hold them all up as he "discovered" them for the children to see. "A game, a mirror, and a dollar bill. Nothing wrong with them in themselves," he'd explain. "*Unless they get more important to us than the Lord.* As masters, they can ruin your life. But the love of the Lord Jesus is more nourishing than a good thick slice of bread and butter. He alone is the Bread of Life."

The queer thing was that the adults seemed to listen more eagerly even than the children. "Sometimes I think I should cut out the adult sermon entirely and just leave the children's," Lee told Myrtie. "When the wisest man who ever lived wanted to get an idea across, he told about men going fishing, a woman losing a piece of money. Everyday crises."

But Lee could be an orator, too, whose words could lead an awed congregation up the weary way to the terrible Cross of Golgotha.

Myrtie always dreaded Palm Sunday, for it was then Lee preached what the whole family called "Dad's Crown Sermon." "He always gets so wet with perspiration, I'm afraid he'll get pneumonia," Myrtie worried as she, and Ike and I (he and I home from school for the Easter holidays) filed into the front row, the preacher's pew where we would sit, suffering through this sermon with Dad. "But last Palm Sunday, after he'd finished, fifty people came up to shake your Dad's hand, wanting to join the church. There's something so—so real about the way he tells what happened. Maybe it's worth what it costs him. . . . I don't know!"

"Crown Him with Many Crowns" was Lee's text for the day. He would list them as he went along: there was the crown of gold for earthly power; the crown of laurel of physical prowess; the crown of Solomon for learning.

"But what kind of crown did they offer the King of Kings?" Lee would ask, his voice ringing in the quiet nave of the church like the tolling of a great sorrowful bell. Standing there in the high pulpit, he would change under our very eyes: his shoulders would droop under the heavy Cross; his face would become white, drawn, beaded with sweat as he climbed the bitter heights of Golgotha. *He was there*: and because he was, we were there too. We couldn't look away, but shivered and climbed with him—and with the Master. We could feel the jostlings of the excited, hostile crowd spitting and kicking at the tired Jesus; shudder with the two frightened thieves also about to be crucified; hear the clanging, implacable footsteps of the Roman guard. Finally came the crash of the hammer, driving the cruel nails through cringing human flesh—"the terrible sound that shivered through the streets of Jerusalem."

"But upon the head of the King of Kings was only a crown of thorns and blood!" Lee would cry. Then, when it seemed we couldn't bear this horror an instant longer, he would swoop down to comfort us. "The way we react to the Cross shows what kind of people we are fundamentally. The thief who was crucified beside Jesus probably never had known a really good man before, but when he met Goodness, he wanted it for himself. Why didn't Jesus take the second thief to heaven with him too? Because he wouldn't have been happy there! But to the thief who yearned for Goodness, he promised immediate action. '*This day* shalt thou be with me in paradise!' " As Lee's agonized eyes swept the congregation, each listener was sure it was he alone into whose very heart Lee was looking, as he asked, "Are you big enough to accept this crown of life eternal? Will you die unto yourself but be alive unto Almighty God?"

After this sermon Lee did not shake hands with the congregation at Trinity's door as usual after the service; he was so exhausted that Ike had to drive him home. It frightened Myrtie to find Lee lying there upon his study couch, his eyes closed, the shadow of death still dark upon his face. All she could think of was the Master, hard-pressed and jostled by the crowd, asking fantastically, "Who touched me?" Myrtie tiptoed out of the study, crying, for she had no part in this Lee upon his mountaintop of Golgotha.

Yet, strangely perhaps, Lee did not consider his preaching as important as being a good pastor to his flock. "Anyone can orate in the pulpit, but he's got to have a *real* inner flame to light the home altar," he used to say.

He now had a church office with a secretary to keep track of his engagements and to write his letters; he was assisted also by an efficient deaconess, whose appearance with her little black bonnet, white silk strings tied under her firm chin, was a welcome sight in all the church homes; but whenever any member of his church was in trouble, Lee always went himself, at any hour, day or night.

"But I don't want an assistant minister"—Lee refused the offer of his official board, who worried over his wearing himself out rushing about a parish of 1400 members. "When folks are sick or in trouble, having a baby or dying, they don't want to see a young cub hardly dry yet behind the ears," he said frankly. "*They want the minister.*"

"Then let us buy you a new car," the official board parried. "One that's sure to get there." For Lee's ancient car had practically rattled to dry bones.

We called the new car "Jehu" because it "driveth furiously." Lee roared happily about town in the big, new, bright-red car, rarely taking his foot off the accelerator. As he drove along, he might be composing his next Sunday's sermon; wondering how to tactfully get rid of a Sunday-school teacher who knew nothing about teaching; or maybe just chatting with the Lord about what a nice day He'd made. Lee had a childlike faith that everything would get out of his way, but frequently an inanimate object did not. Once he absently took the top off of a water hydrant with Jehu's bumper and was almost drowned before he came out of his dream long enough to figure out what had happened.

But since Lee and the mayor of Worcester, not to mention the chief of police, were good friends, the traffic cops hesitated to arrest the absent-minded minister for anything less than actual manslaughter. One day as Lee drove through the center of town at forty miles an hour with pedestrians leaping right and left for safety zones, one traffic cop did halt the big red Jehu.

"Now, now, Father Nies," the cop protested, removing his cap to wipe his still sweating brow, "is it anyone dyin' now? If he ain't, he will be soon. If you don't drive more careful, I'll have to give ye a ticket!"

"Go right ahead, Patrick," Lee urged contritely. "I'd give me a ticket if I were you!"

Ike was away studying at Wilberham Academy; Myrtie drove a car only in a series of bunny hops; but when I came home from college during the week ends, I'd drive Dad around on his calls so Mother wouldn't worry. After she'd been called to the hospital to bail Dad out from a few cuts and bruises he'd collected in fortunately minor accidents, she seldom heard the phone ring while Lee was out without leaping fearfully to answer. During these rides with Dad I learned more than in any college classroom: I learned that the hardest thing in the world is to just be yourself, not swayed by every wind of fact or fancy; that Dad's being "wise as a serpent and harmless as a dove" was both an art and a philosophy.

One spring afternoon I was driving Dad out into the far suburbs of Worcester to call on a parishioner who was, Lee said, so ill that only prayer could help him now.

I looked at Dad from the dizzy height of my sophomore course in psychology. "I'm afraid I don't believe in religious shibboleths any more," I announced loftily. "Prayer—let's face it!—is simply talking to yourself, with therapeutic value as an emotional cathartic, doubtless," I conceded kindly. Hopefully I braced myself for shocked disapproval, but none came. Instead Dad looked at the moth which had flown in the open car window; he held out his finger and the little creature with gray-velvet wings alighted there, quivering. "Can you give life to even a moth, Susie?" Dad asked, mild as new milk. "Can Freud? Hmm. Well, God can." The moth waved its gray wings a couple of times, then drifted again out the window. "What's more to the point," Dad said more sternly, "can you make a moth make itself? Out of a worm?"

There didn't seem to be any answer to that one; but I detoured gamely. "At least you'll agree that the miracles were not historical facts but religious allegories, designed to teach a truth? I don't believe in sin either," I warmed to my subject. "How can you help who your ancestors were? Or the traits you inherited from them? Nobody can be sinful, truly, just natural or unnatural."

"A miracle is perfectly natural," Dad admitted at once. "For God. Science mounts on an ascending staircase of discarded 'facts.' What is today's 'miracle' may be tomorrow's commonplace. I suppose you could call some of the miracles of healing 'pyschosomatic medicine'—but that wouldn't change what happened, merely the name. Many miracles are only a speeding up of time, which doesn't exist with God anyway."

"But time *does* exist!" I protested, a little wildly. "We're in it!"

"Time is relative, just as size is relative," Dad pointed out calmly. "You can hide the sun with a penny if you hold it close enough to your eye. To a hungry baby five minutes of yelling for its bottle is an aeon. To God a thousand years are as a day." Dad smiled at me and slid a big arm down from the back of the seat around my shoulders, and his finger was roughly tender against my cheek as he murmured, "Maybe some people wouldn't call it a miracle, my having a dear child like you, sprung from the joining of two particles too small to be seen with the naked eye. But I do. I call it God."

Somewhat shaken, I went back to college, but in every class I went into I heard Lee's quiet words, "I call it God." Scientists, I admitted, gave arbitrary names also to things they never saw, atoms, protons, and neutrons; but these were none the less real because they were invisible. Even the desk I sat at was not solid as it seemed, but a mass of whirling energy held together by law: doubtless everything but the human soul could be reduced to a deathless energy that could change its form but never be lost. What did it matter if you called this "deathless energy," or "God," as Dad did?

But it did matter. How could you talk to whirling, sightless, deathless energy? Yet with my own ears I had heard Lee talk to God, and from this derive strength. As a scientist, I had to admit observed phenomena. Once again I was a frightened little girl squatting outside Lee's study door, listening to him wrestle with the Lord for Myrtie's life, when Bildad died. When Lee picked me up and held me closely in his arms, he had known his Myrtie was going to live! Some energy, some certainty, some power had passed from God to Dad, and from him to me. The poets of the Bible said this in a different way.

" 'And underneath are the everlasting arms,' " I murmured aloud into my physics books open before me on my desk.

My college roommate looked up, startled, from her own book. "Talking to yourself?"

"No," I said slowly. "I was praying."

It was small wonder that the June I received my golden Phi Beta Kappa key, I laid it in Dad's big palm, where it looked extremely small and unimportant. "This belongs to you, for teaching me to think—a little," I said.

"Good grief," Dad chuckled. "Nobody's grown till they've lived through Santa Claus and Freud—and don't think I don't believe in both of 'em! You will too, if you're as smart as I think you are." He tried to smooth down his tumbled hair and only made it worse, for he always ran his fingers through it when his sermon wouldn't jell. "How about going to the movies?" he said. "Jake gave me passes."

Just why the movies should be considered legitimate for a Methodist minister and his family to attend while the legitimate stage was not has always seemed to me a strange paradox. Possibly the advent of the movies merely came at a propitious time when the need for inexpensive public entertainment was paramount; just as Henry Ford cashed in upon the crying need for a cheap car the average man could afford. In any case, Dad loved the drama that flitted across the screen; he lived every action, every emotion as avidly as the actors themselves.

"Come often, Mr. Nies," urged Jake, the little Jewish proprietor, as we went out of our neighborhood movie house. "When you laugh, it is catching like measles!"

"At least the story wasn't all entrails and bastards," Lee remarked as we drove home. "I never could understand why they called that stuff *realism*. You can hardly pick up a book nowadays that doesn't concentrate on bedrooms and bathrooms. For heaven's sake, if you ever do write, Susie, tell the *whole* truth; even coal isn't all smut; it burns with a clear warm light to keep you warm."

The parsonage at Worcester had need of laughter, for it was a big, dark Victorian house with stained-glass windows in the front hall which turned you blue or morbid green as you entered. And the house was too large for Myrtie to care for alone.

She suffered through a series of ill-paid, incompetent help who were always precipitating social crises when least expected. One girl just over from Ireland boiled the lettuce thinking it a peculiar kind of American cabbage and let the ice cream melt while she wrestled with the three-layer cake Myrtie had spent all morning baking and decorating. Finally in triumph Bridget produced a few frosted crumbs, announcing, "It stuck together something terrible!" Unless watched, "Minnie the Monk," as we kids called Bridget's successor, used to shut the kitten up in the linen closet when its mewing annoyed her, and she quit the job when Mother insisted that all the linen be washed.

Entertaining under such conditions was nervewracking, to say the least. Myrtie was struggling with another new maid who spoke only two words of English: "sure!" and "wadjawant?" when Ike arrived home on Thanksgiving vacation from Wilberham Academy with a mountain of luggage and two Siamese princes.

"They were lonesome, Mom, and had no place to go." Ike explained his oriental royalty casually. "Is Susie bringing anyone home from college, so there won't be room?"

"No, she gets in alone on the three o'clock train, dear," Myrtie murmured. "Will you boys meet her?" She looked dubiously after the chubby princes disappearing into the blue bedroom, after having displayed so far only deep bows and wide smiles. "Do they speak English? With Tinka talking only Hungarian, it might be awkward." Ike said that certainly they talked English but not much American, and that we were to call them just "Chula" and "Izzy" because their Siamese names were quite unpronounceable.

Entertaining royalty proved to have its moments. Chula and Izzy, used to being waited on hand and foot at their home palace, dropped their clothes wherever they happened to be dressing, in bathroom or bedroom, and put their shoes outside the door every night to be shined. Tinka refused to shine them, and Ike forgot, so Dad, chuckling, took over as bootboy. When the three boys met

me at the station with the car, Chula and Izzy never raised their
eyes to mine when introduced, just stared at the station platform.
In fact, they never did speak to me directly, nor would they even
pass me the salt at the dinner table that night; they simply pretended I wasn't there.

"Listen, I may be no Cleopatra, but I'm not that bad," I told Ike
darkly. "Why don't you teach your crowned heads some man-
ners?"

Dad, who was always for getting at the root of any problem at
once, inquired of Chula and Izzy what was the matter with Susie?
They showed Dad their notebook full of items they had promised
to avoid while studying in the United States; especially were they
to remain good Buddhists and under no circumstances were either
of them to bring home an American wife.

"But Susie wouldn't think of marrying you!" Dad assured them,
shocked.

"Is wonderful!" beamed Chula. They'd been terrified lest I interpret even an offer of salt as a step toward matrimony. Once assured
of their safety, the two princes vied so in buying me expensive
jewelry that Myrtie had to explain to them again the facts of life
concerning the bewildering *jeune fille Américaine*. Whereupon
they invested in so many flowers and boxes of expensive note-
paper, I wouldn't be surprised if there were some still floating about
the Worcester parsonage attic.

An international tension arose one evening at dinner time when
Tinka rushed into the dining room brandishing a large broom instead of the dessert and making loud, frightened noises in Hungarian. Dad investigated, announcing that there was a mouse in the
kitchen but that he'd kill it pronto.

"No!" Chula leaped from his chair and ran out to the kitchen,
hopping up and down and protesting violently. "Maybe aunt in
mouse! Perhaps grandmother!"

"Well, if she is, she'd probably like to get out," said Dad pro-
ceeding calmly with the delivery of auntie with his broom.

Since there was no Buddhist service available, the two princes
politely went to hear Lee preach next Sunday at Trinity Church,
but he said later that they sat there like two graven images, deter-

mined to hear no evil, see no evil, speak no evil. He could fairly hear Buddhist prayers twanging about his Methodist ears, and which got to the good God quicker it was hard to say.

Lee could always see the funny side of any situation, but there was no malice, only understanding, in his laughter. He laughed with the world, not at it. He always used to scold us when Ike and I giggled at prayer meeting when "Teeta" testified about "the tat tame back." Since Lee's coming, attendance at prayer meeting on Wednesday nights had more than doubled, crowding the vestry to the doors. The last fifteen minutes of the service were always given over to "testimony," and Teeta was always first to leap to her feet. She had an impediment in her speech as well as in her mental processes and always told the same story, how she'd lost her cat but the Lord had sent it back to her. We kids called her Teeta because she invariably asked for the hymn "We Shall See the King Some Day," as "Teeta Teeta Ting Tum Tay."

"The Lord didn't come only to college students," Dad would say sternly. "Nor did He give everyone ten talents. Some day that poor woman may surprise you."

That was no understatement. One morning Teeta appeared, dirty and unkempt, at the parsonage front door, holding something wrapped in the sleeve of her overcoat, something that squalled. Could it be her "tat that tame back"?

"It's a baby! A little baby!" Myrtie gasped. "Where on earth did you get it—er—her?"

The baby was her own niece, Teeta explained. Her sister had died, leaving no one to take care of the baby but her. But the district nurse wanted to take the baby away from her! Panic rose in Teeta's broad, homely face as she promised, "But I'll keep her clean, clean. I love babies. Please, Mr. Nies, tell them I gotta keep her!"

Lee was convinced that the regenerative power of a great love might cleanse Teeta's whole way of living. Affection, Lee insisted, was at least as important for babies as antiseptics in an orphan's home; so he stood sponsor for Teeta and her baby to the scandalized town authorities. "But the minute they see you aren't taking good care of your baby, they'll take her away!" he warned.

Teeta scrubbed the kitchen floor so hard it splintered, and even scrubbed herself. When the little girl was old enough to come to Sunday school, her clothes were dainty, hand-smocked, and immaculate. She grew up loved and loving and very bright in public school; the last I heard she was teaching the first grade and taking care of her happy, tongue-tied aunt who no longer went out as a scrubwoman.

Dad's experiments in practical psychology usually worked because it was the individual people he thought of, rather than the theory. He did believe in many of Freud's theories of human behavior; but Dad believed even more in the regenerative power of a God who had made these natural laws and so could bend them to His will. To Lee it was all "poppycock" that a man couldn't change what his ancestors had made of him. It was exactly his free will that made him a son of God! Certainly there were the spider and the butterfly, the devil and the angel, in each of us; but we could choose which one would be triumphant—with God's help. We could obtain this God power only as we *chose* to connect our lives with it; just as you have to plug in a lamp into the electric house current before it will light up the room. Long before Alcoholics Anonymous had made their great discovery of the regenerative power of friendship and prayer, Dad was teaching his "down-and-outers," as Ike and I called them as they knelt in our front parlor, the way back to mental health.

An organizer for a fraternal order came to Dad's study one day, in abject terror of losing his job. He'd started hard drinking "to be a good fellow" and the habit had grown on him till he'd been warned that one more "lost week end" would be his last with the organization.

"I'm ashamed to confess that I just can't leave alcohol alone any more," he said, his hands shaking, his bloodshot eyes desperate. "Disgrace is staring me in the face. My uncle who owns a big fishing fleet down at the Cape sent me to the hospital for treatment the last time; but the 'cure' lasted only a few weeks. If you don't stop me, I'll go out of here to the nearest saloon. *Can you help me?*"

"No," Lee said flatly. Then as the other man's face twitched, "But I have a friend who can, Ed."

"Who is it?"

"Jesus Christ."

"You're just saying that professionally." The other man shrugged. "You don't really believe that."

"Well, it worked for Atwood," Lee told him, naming another man high up in the organizer's own society. Ed looked startled; he hadn't even known that Atwood ever took a drink, he said. "He doesn't—now," Lee said. "He hasn't for ten years. Not since he surrendered that habit he couldn't control to the Lord, who could. He lost his craving for alcohol *on his knees.*"

"If Jesus Christ can cure Atwood, he can cure me," the shaking alcoholic said. He held out his hand to Lee. "I'm going back to my hotel to pray. Will you come to me if I need you?"

For three days Lee shuttled back and forth from the parsonage to the hotel, praying that alcoholic through. On the fourth day Ed rose to his feet, a new man with his face shining, his eyes clear and his hands steady. He said, "I'm going right downstairs to telegraph my Uncle Doane at Wellfleet what has happened to me! He should be in port, by now, as I am!"

Ed brought the answer proudly back to the parsonage for Lee to read:

"When I got your telegram I was so happy I broke out a brand-new American flag before the mast!" his Uncle Doane wired. "The other crews came around, wanted to know what all the excitement was about. I said, 'It's a great day! My Ed's just met Jesus Christ!'"

Ed was one of the reasons Lee got such a kick out of his job as a minister. Chris Crane was another, for he paid back every cent his fellow official board members had advanced him when he had been nearly arrested as a common thief. But his friends had given him more than money when they let him stay on as head usher at the church. As Lee watched Chris marching down the aisle, as erect as ever, his silver head high, the brave white carnation still in his buttonhole, Lee thought, "If we kept out everyone who had fallen down into the valley, we wouldn't have any church. The minister's big job is to light a bonfire up on the mountain peak to guide his people back to God, through the dark."

CHAPTER 12

Fling Out the Stars

UNDER LEE'S LEADERSHIP, Trinity Church, already a smoothly working machine, was speeded up into high gear, and boasted the largest membership of any Methodist church in New England. But Lee took small pride in this; he was too shattered by the advent of World War I, which he took as a personal catastrophe. As in the case of his Human Fly, he felt that our sins of omission implicated us all; if all Christians had been really Christlike, including himself, Germany would not have been a bloodthirsty thug rampaging through Europe. So though he did not believe that war ever settled any controversy, he felt he must have a part in it; he must go, as he was sure Jesus Christ would go, into the battlefield with his boys from Trinity. But when Lee volunteered as chaplain, he was turned down because the doctors discovered that he had incipient diabetes. Such black dejection settled down over Lee's spirit that he found it hard to preach.

"The first time my country needs me and I'm no good," he groaned to Myrtie when he found her out in the kitchen beating up a cake and told her his bad news (all except the doctor's diagnosis, which he kept to himself). "What am I going to say to the parents of my boys when the telegram comes that they're gone, and I'm still here, sitting on my fat fanny?"

Myrtie didn't answer him, just went right on beating, absorbed in making her cake. Women were wonderful, Lee thought, watching the little curls at the back of Myrtie's neck as she stood there in her crisp pink house dress, slapping her hand into the yellow bowl; in time of crisis they always found something that needed doing. Myrtie could stand there, calmly going on with her business of feeding her family, while nations toppled. Over in France, probably, after the bombing was over, the French mothers picked up the pieces of their shattered kitchens and began getting supper. Women were the creators of life. Men wrecked the homes with bombs, and women cried, and picked up the splinters with their bleeding fingers; and life grew big within them again when their men came home. . . .

Lee left the kitchen abruptly and when his study door slammed, Myrtie knew, with relief, that he'd gone to talk over the whole bitter problem of what his war contribution was to be with his Friend. When Lee came out again, his face was shining and his eyes were at peace.

"There'll be a great many go from our church and I'll write to them every week," he planned to Myrtie. "About what's going on in their crowd, how Mom looks, and that the old jalopy's still running—little homey things you think of when you're away." He chuckled, "Trinity Gossip Column"; and then his face grew grave. "And we'll start special meetings next week, at the church, for deepening our knowledge of God. If we can't stand beside our boys, we can back them up with prayer."

"You might throw in a miracle or two so they'll all come home," Myrtie suggested, her eyes suddenly dark with shadows, for she had a son of her own. Ike was too young to go yet, but he'd finish his freshman year at Wesleyan College this spring, and if the war lasted long enough. . . . She shivered, drew herself together, and passed Lee a well-filled plate of cake. "It's your favorite gold cake with chocolate frosting," she told him. "You better take two pieces. If this sugar shortage gets any worse, we just won't have any more."

The doctor had told Lee he must never eat any more sugar, but he couldn't stop Myrtie's practical way of comforting him just yet.

He ate his piece of cake to the last crumb, knowing that tomorrow a new era must now begin for him as for the world.

The silken service flag at Trinity lengthened frighteningly over the next six months; 121 boys and 4 nurses went to the war from Lee's congregation. Then the gold stars began to appear, also, on his church flag. Lee might have lost his own sons, he grieved for them so. When he heard the bad news, he went at once to the boy's home and stayed as long as the family—his family—needed him, letting all other business pile up on his desk.

"He didn't preach at us or pray—out loud," one mother told Myrtie gratefully after Lee had spent the entire night with the family when the fateful telegram from Washington came. "But we knew he was praying, as we were, for his face was so quiet and calm. All I could think of was how the Bible says that Enoch walked with God in the cool of the evening. Sometimes I think just being still and listening for God is the best kind of prayer."

Not all mothers were able to take their loss in this greatness of spirit, for the peace that passes understanding does not come to every man in the same way. "The prayer of action is needed as well as the prayer in words" was the way Lee put it to Myrtie. "We have to *accept* the peace."

One day he arrived at a home to find the husband distracted and the wife close to hysteria. She'd been working up attic and run across an old baseball bat that her boy used to use and it had brought back memories too painful to bear. She sobbed to Lee, "I don't want to wait till eternity to see my Johnny! I want him right now!"

"Throw that bat away, Mary," her husband urged. "It's just tearing you to pieces."

But Lee took up the bat the boy would never use again, hefting it in his hand. "No, Mary, I'd keep it. I often think that things like this that are left behind are a real part of immortality. Maybe our thinking about Johnny, loving him, will help him to bat a homer wherever he is now!" He told the mother gently, "We do not know what the next life will be like for those who love the Lord like Johnny did; but two things are sure: we will all come to it and it will be beautiful." When Lee handed the bat back to Johnny's mother, the handle was warm again where his hand had held it, not a cold, dead thing; and her heart had warmed strangely too.

Lee kept his word about backing up the boys who were away from home, by the prayers of their friends. He had always insisted, "If I can get a whole church praying, the power to do everything else flows in." The boys' families and friends flocked to these meetings where Lee said, as he'd told Molly Stark years before, "The only way whole families that are separated can get together, no matter where the members are, around the breakfast table or on the battlefield, is in prayer.

> *"For so the whole round world is everywhere*
> *Bound by gold chains about the feet of God."*

Every Wednesday Lee would discuss a different kind of prayer, illustrating by telling a simple story from his experience. So many worried, heart-hungry people thronged to hear these real-life stories of the power of prayer that the vestry grew too small, and had to be enlarged.

"Lee has the common touch all right," one official member murmured one evening, looking around at the crowd, but another member whispered back, "No, he has the God-touch."

"The love of God is like a mother's prayer; it never lets her boy go," Lee began one evening. "This incident happened when I was very young, supplying a small chapel in Dallas, Texas. The closing hymn had just been sung and I was raising my hand for the benediction when a big strapping six-foot Texas ranger in uniform came striding down the church aisle.

"Don't close the meeting yet, Preacher!" he begged. "What were the words of that hymn you-all were just singing?"

> *"Just as I am, without one plea*
> *But that Thy blood was shed for me."*

Lee quoted, "Why, friend?"

"That's the one!" the ranger cried, his face lighting. "That's my mother's song. She prayed for me, too. She prayed, 'God bless my poor little boy, Jimmy!' That prayer has followed me for thirty years. Preacher, can you tell me how to pray to my mother's God?"

As the tall ranger slid to his knees at the altar railing, Lee motioned to several of his church members who came and knelt beside him to pray too. "A strange thing happened," Lee related to his breathless, listening congregation in Worcester. "That whole church was filled with the glory of God. Time no longer existed, nor life nor death nor earth nor heaven, for they were all one, lost in the vastness of God. Above the kneeling people you could almost hear those who had washed their robes and made them white in the blood of the Lamb."

After the meeting was over, the Texas ranger told Lee his almost incredible story. Just before he was born, he said, his father had deserted his mother, and the shame of this may have been one reason she died. When Jimmy's mother knew she was going, she had the nurse bring the baby to her, sang him a hymn as a lullaby. Then she put her two hands over her baby's head and prayed, "Oh God, take care of him. He hasn't any father but You. God bless my boy Jimmy!"

The scene impressed the nurse so that she adopted the boy as her own, and at bedtime she'd tell him how his mother had prayed and would sing him his mother's song, over and over. But since the nurse had to be away working, as he grew older Jimmy roamed the streets. He felt terribly alone; no one wanted him really, so he compensated for his loneliness by picking fights. The neighbors called him a big bully; and maybe he was. One day in schoolyard, in a rage, he picked up his slate from which the binding had come off, leaving a sharp edge, and hit another boy over the head. The boy screamed, "You've killed me!" and fell to the ground, with blood pouring from his head. Jimmy ran. He ran and ran. He didn't dare even go home for fear of being picked up by the police. He hitch-hiked clear to Galveston, where he shipped as cabin boy on a sailing vessel. But even there he did not feel really safe. When the ship was in port, Jimmy didn't go ashore for fear he was still wanted by the police for murder.

It was ten years before Jimmy dared go back to Dallas—and the very first night he saw the name of the boy he thought he'd killed up on a brightly lighted sign over a big department store! The man he hadn't killed turned out to be a powerful politician, and again became his friend. He got Jimmy a job as Texas ranger, which was no sinecure. For ten years Jimmy had been fighting cattle thieves, the Indians who still roamed the plains, and what was worse, the city thugs who went out to terrorize the country-side. But Jimmy knew that the medals he got for bravery didn't belong to him at all; they belonged to his mother; no bullet was made that could pierce the armor of his mother's protecting prayer.

"Tonight when I heard you singing here in the church, I thought to myself, 'My mother's prayer has taken care of me all my life, and has followed me all over the world,' Jimmy told Lee as the two of them stayed behind when the rest of the congregation left. "So I came in to pray too."

Lee's eyes looked out over his Worcester people as he ended Jimmy's story, but he wasn't seeing the crowded room or even that chapel in Dallas so long ago; he was seeing a lonely sentry standing in a trench, listening for the advance of the enemy that would mean he must kill or be killed. The sentry was God's child too, and so was the enemy. What should you pray? Lee's long gaze came back to his people in Worcester as he murmured, "Jesus Christ alone knows all the answers—to our personal problems, to those of a sorrowing world. He has promised to be wherever two or three are gathered together. Let us bow our heads and be at one with Him, and with our sons and daughters who are away from us for a little while, but who are at home with God."

Lee never used sentiment as a goad to worship; he merely accepted emotion as a natural part of life. He believed firmly that this bundle of instincts, dreams, and subconscious wish-fulfillments we call 'man' could be integrated by Christ into a body and soul worthy of inheriting eternal life as a son of God. "Emotion alone can become a sickish stink," he remarked. "But those who pride themselves on being 'coldly intellectual' merely drive their emotions inward, only to have them burst out later in an unhealthy flood. Do not be ashamed of your emotions, but bridle them as you do a spirited horse."

But the night that Lee told the story of the Texas ranger, he was startled to have a man rush up to him after the meeting with his eyes blazing with anger. "How can you say that God's love is like a mother's!" he spoke excitedly to Lee. "I hated my mother. She was a devil!"

Lee took the stranger into his study where he could pour out his story in private. "I had a sister I loved," he explained. "When she didn't do what my mother ordered, she'd knock her clear across the room! She threw me about too until I got so big I was afraid I'd hit her back—so I ran away from home. But I kept in touch with my sister and last week I got a letter telling me my mother was dead, to come home for her funeral." The young man's eyes were bright with hate as he asked Lee, "You know what I was thinking when they lowered my mother's casket into the grave? 'There,' I thought. 'You'll never hit my sister again!' "

"Do you like music?" Lee asked abruptly. He drew the bewildered stranger after him out into the now empty vestry and sat down at the piano. For nearly an hour Lee played and sang while the stranger listened, slumped in his chair. When he was sure the other man was calm again Lee told him quietly, "Hate is a two-edged sword. It will hurt you all your life. *You must throw your hate away*. You will never have peace until you forgive your mother. Let's talk to the Lord about it."

They prayed together all night and in the morning Lee brought the lad back to the parsonage with him. After one look at their tired faces, Myrtie whipped up a batch of her delicious muffins and made the coffee extra strong. She said as she passed the now peaceful boy his cup, "I don't believe I know your name."

Lee and his new friend stared at each other, startled. "Come to think of it," Lee chuckled, "I don't believe I do, either."

"The Two Old Maids of Salem" was the title of Lee's Wednesday-night story about the power of prayer that is lived rather than spoken. Lee's study in this particular church had a narrow little stained-glass window showing the Master helping a tired lamb over a stile; one evening when Lee was working there late, a knock came at his study door. The man to whom Lee opened the door wore a tall silk hat, handsome clothes, and his resonant voice proclaimed him a trained speaker.

"Your window is so lovely with the light shining through," the tall man said, seating himself with ease beside Lee's study desk.

"The workmanship is so fine. That lamb now, being helped so tenderly over the high stile . . ." Suddenly his cultured voice broke, becoming harsh, and his mouth twisted in a cry from the heart. "Sir!" he gasped. "Can you help me over my stile?"

"Tell me about you," Lee urged.

The tall man grimaced. "I'm what you might call a 'professional atheist,' I guess. I lecture against religion. The climax of my talk has always been for me to take out my watch and cry, 'I dare God—if there is a God—to strike me dead! I give Him five minutes!' Of course," the stranger admitted, "it was only a publicity stunt, but it got me a full house, it gave the audience such chills."

He waited for Lee to say something, but when he didn't, the lecturer, running his nervous fingers round and round the top of his smooth tall hat, went on, "One night when I was lecturing in Salem, I fainted. I'd had a bad cold, had no business being out at all, but I needed the money. Business hadn't been too good. The ambulance was just about to take me to the hospital where I would have had to go into the charity ward, when two old maids who had been in my audience interfered. One said to the other, 'We have a spare room, Jenny. Let's take this man home with us and take care of him.'

"I had pneumonia. Those two old maids took care of me for six weeks!" the stranger told Lee. "Their bedroom was next to mine so they could hear if I called, and every night before they got into bed, I'd hear the murmur of their voices. I couldn't make out the words, but *I knew they were praying for me*. It—it got on my nerves, but I never said a word about it and neither did they. When I left, I asked those two old maids how much I owed them and they said 'Not a cent! We were glad to have you.' " The lecturer's voice rose to almost a cry as he told Lee, "Those two old characters just looked at each other and I knew perfectly well why they'd taken care of me, a stranger who defied their God. *They did it for Jesus' sake*." He was shouting now. "Anybody those two women believed in so deeply has to be real. Can you introduce me to Jesus Christ?"

Lee smiled as he looked out over his Worcester congregation

waiting, fascinated, to hear the end of the story. "That man is now a preacher in a church not far from here. No, don't ask his name. When he wants it known, he'll tell his own story. But perhaps he's wise to keep it a story without words, as was the prayer of the two old maids of Salem."

It seemed a pitiful thing to Lee, the way people were hungry to hear how to pray and yet were not willing to surrender their wills to the Lord's, without which no real prayer is possible. For prayer to him was a real weapon. The horror stories that filled the daily newspapers were not about strange men fighting but concerned our own boys, from Trinity, from Worcester, from all over this big land. Through prayer we could put into their hands not the conquest of their enemies but of themselves—"the power to reach up to touch the face of God." Lee explained night after night, "Prayer is keeping open the channels of communication with God, for to do His will is the only peace for any of us."

"Many person's prayers are wicked," Lee said sternly. "They merely try to use God as a convenience to change the weather, to bring them success in business, to kill their enemies. To trade with God—if you'll do this for me, then I'll do that for you—is heathen. You might as well turn a prayer wheel as the Buddhists do! Some prayers are mere superstitions. 'I'd better say my prayers, for if I don't, something might happen to me!' These are the same child-ish people who won't walk on a crack in the sidewalk and have to look at the moon over their left shoulder. Others, lacking faith, pray, thinking to themselves, 'If you want something, I notice you have to hustle for it!' It never occurs to them *that God might be giving them the strength to hustle!* The man with polio doesn't walk very far. All these prayers," Lee insisted, "go only as far as a person's nose, and make merely an unpleasant smell before the Lord."

"What then is real prayer?"

"It is not wheedling things out of God or telling Him how to run the universe as so many preachers do at length on a Sunday morning. *Every true prayer starts with God.* Prayer is His will for us coming through the channels of our willingness to listen. Man's patent of divinity is that he may choose God or turn Him away. When we pray, 'Thy will be done,' we open the flood gate of greatness which the Lord has planned for every soul. Only as we catch his spirit and purpose and something of his burden for the sins of the whole world can we pray, 'Our Father.' And until we can include in this 'Our' every man, black, white or yellow, or brown, we will never have world peace."

Fervent, effectual prayer, Lee insisted, was the only way known to man or science by which a man's character could permanently be changed; heredity and environment might make him a thief or a scholar, but *he did not have to stay a thief*. To talk about "besetting sins" as if they were something we could not control was twaddle. In proof of this on his last Wednesday-night discussion of what prayer could do, Lee told the story of "Greg Stone Dies Tonight."

The minister whom Lee was to follow at the Framingham Church had warned Lee before he left town about this man, Greg Stone. "I don't usually say a word about anyone in the parish, but I feel I must warn you that Greg is breaking up the church," the worried minister said.

"He welcomed me very cordially this morning," Lee protested, a trifle coldly, for he liked to make up his own mind about his new parishioners.

"He would," the other minister agreed bitterly, for Greg Stone had been responsible for his leaving this pleasant town. "But just cross him and see what happens! You can't quite put your finger on what he does, but he turns every committee he's on into a three-ring circus unless he's chairman. He insulted me once at the Sunday-school picnic. . . . Oh, I know that sounds like a little thing, but . . . well, I just thought I'd warn you."

Lee tried not to be prejudiced about Greg Stone, but he soon saw that the former pastor had been right. Greg was a big, powerful man with a shock of black hair, a vibrant personality, and a voice you could hear six blocks away; he wasn't taking any back talk from anyone, he boasted, not even the minister.

"Some folks are born to lead as surely as others have a wart on the chin or a game leg," Lee said. "And Greg would have been a leader even if he didn't have more money than anyone else in the church. You could see all the parish were watching covertly for the clash between Greg and me, when he tried to boss me as he had all the other ministers. So I decided to meet the situation head on, instead of waiting for it to eventuate."

Lee preached one Sunday on "Besetting Sins," with Greg sitting in a front seat, and he used an illustration from the evangelist Sam Jones. "It's a kind of rough story," Lee told his Worcester parish, "that doesn't tie in with these wishy-washy ideas some folks think is religion—the kind who paint the disciples as consumptives in white bathrobes—but the story hit Greg Stone right where he lived. I could see him leaning forward, fascinated.

"If I set a trap for a mink," Sam Jones used to say, "and my hound dog got himself caught in the trap, I'd forgive him and let him loose, because he didn't know any better. But if he did the same fool thing the next day and the next, I'd get my shotgun and shoot him! He'd be absolutely no good, anyway. Yet you people listening to me out there keep on repeating the same sin day after day. You say smugly, 'Oh that's my besetting sin!' I tell you, you aren't worth the powder and shell to blow you up!"

After Lee had finished his story, he could see from the corner of his eye Greg's face getting redder and redder, so he wasn't surprised when Greg asked to walk home with him after church. He said, "Pastor, that's queer talk you're giving us."

"It's true, isn't it?" Lee asked.

"I'm afraid it is," Greg Stone muttered surprisingly. He stopped under a lamplight, straightened his big shoulders, and looked at Lee. "Pastor," he said, "*I'm that dog!* I've got a temper that scares even me sometimes. . . . Today's my birthday. I'm forty and called a success. But I'm not; I can't even govern myself. Lee, I don't want a lot of church talk; I want it straight, man to man. Can Jesus Christ help me?"

"Yes," Lee shot back at him. "You heard my text tonight, Greg. 'Reckon ye yourselves dead unto sin.' Let the Lord take over, Greg; that's the only way."

"By the grace of God, Greg Stone dies tonight!" The big man shot out his hand, gripped Lee's till it was nearly crushed, and strode off into the night toward his home. Lee didn't follow him;

he knew that a man as strong as this had to fight his way through by himself. But he stayed near the telephone in case Greg should ask for his help. A day went by, two days. Lee visited Greg's place of business but the big man wasn't there. Lee began to get nervous; he decided he'd go to Greg's house after prayer meeting that night to find out what had happened.

But Greg Stone came to the meeting himself. He came marching down the aisle as if trumpets were blowing, and the look on his face was "high and lifted up." Lee said without sound, "Thank you, Lord!" For he knew without asking that Greg Stone had wrestled with his angel and had won.

Lee preached that night as if his own words had wings. When it came time for testimony, Greg Stone came forward and faced the crowd from the altar railing. "I came here to ask your pardon for a lot of things I've done," Greg said. "I drove the last minister away, as you and I know. But I've been praying for three days and nights. I've made my peace with God, and now I want to make it with you." He turned to smile up at Lee on the platform and murmured, only for his ear and for the Lord's, " 'Thy gentleness hath made me great.' "

"Greg wore the certainty of the presence of God like a royal garment all the rest of his life," Lee told his Worcester congregation. "Twenty boys in his Sunday-school class came to me before the year was done and asked to join the church. I never heard Greg Stone's voice lifted in anger again. He moved away later, became an official in another larger church near Springfield. I heard once that they were having trouble in that church, so when I next saw the District Superintendent, I asked him about Greg Stone, and whether he was still an official member."

"He sure is," the District Superintendent said warmly. "Come to think of it, Greg Stone is the only one at that church who hasn't lost his temper!" The District Superintendent grinned sheepishly at Lee, adding, "Including me!"

All of Lee's "war work" however wasn't confined to Worcester. During his six years at Trinity, he was twice elected delegate to General Conferences of the Methodist Church, the first held at Saratoga Springs, New York, and the second in Des Moines, Iowa.

Lee became known to so many delegates as a man to whom clarity
of the spirit was more important than the letter of the law that he
was appointed a member of the national Committee on Evangelism.
This group of church leaders went from Maine to California, speaking to thousands, reminding them that this terrible war would be
fought in vain, unless out of it came some greatness of spirit, a
lifting up of the banner of God. Thus only could we achieve the
inner quietness which is the only lasting basis of peace between
men and nations. Lee preached in many great pulpits with such
power that he was offered pastorates in Ohio, California, and
Texas. He thanked the committees but turned them down.

"New England is my home now," Lee explained. "I am no longer
a young man. When I finish my active ministry, all I want is to
go back to the little church in Townsend where I began; to hear
its great bell go tolling God among the quiet little hills."

Offers of honorary degrees, of a professorship in a great theological school poured in upon this successful pastor of the big
"family church" at Worcester, but Lee accepted only one. He
went back to Oklahoma City to receive the honorary degree of
Doctor of Divinity from Oklahoma City University, which had
absorbed the old Texas Wesleyan college at Fort Worth where
he had won honors as a boy.

"People have called me 'Doctor Nies' for so long, I figure I
ought to legitimatize the bastard," Lee chuckled to Myrtie who was
desolate because they couldn't afford the money for her to go,
too, to see Lee receive his degree. Ike was out of college and I was
supporting myself, but still a preacher's salary didn't stretch to
cover both Lee's expenses and those of the endless procession of
people who needed his cash more than Lee did.

A letter was waiting for Lee when he came home to Worcester,
asking if he would accept the secretaryship of the Board of Evangelism for the whole great Methodist Church, if it were offered to
him. "I'm sure this can be arranged if you want the job, Lee," the
letter ended. "Just let me know." Lee read the letter over several
times before he called Myrtie into his study and handed it to her
without comment. She was a part of his life; what happened to
him happened to her too; she had a right to be heard.

"The last two secretaries were elected bishop!" Myrtie cried, thrilled. She'd always known Lee had a great future, that someday he would be important in the church. . . . But it was a wonderful feeling to find yourself proved right about the man you loved! *Bishop Leopold Adolf Nies*. . . . *Mrs. Bishop Nies*. . . . She planned happily, "A bishop gets a pension for life, so we'd never be a burden on the children. . . ." She stopped, swallowed the old familiar lump of dismay in her throat, for Lee wasn't smiling back at her. He was sitting there too quietly in his chair, staring out the study window so she couldn't read his mind. Myrtie asked, "You don't want the secretary's job, Lee?"

"I like working with people," Lee told her slowly. "I understand them. They tell me intimate things, and let me help them because they know I've been poor too; I know how grinding poverty feels. I've seen birth and death, suffering, even murder. I've lost a child." He saw she wasn't understanding how big was the compulsion within him and burst out, "I'd hate an office in New York. If I'd wanted to push buttons, to be on committees, to be important, I'd have stayed in business. I would have been successful too. But a parish priest's job is the biggest there is."

Myrtie interrupted, her voice trembling, "You don't have to stop helping people just because you're a bishop!"

Lee drew her down into his lap and kissed her. He suggested, "Let's get into Jehu and run up to Newagen to think this thing through, without interruptions. You and I will decide quietly there together, what we want to do."

So they drove the 200 miles over the muddy spring roads to the peaceful Snuggery they both loved. Deep in her mind Myrtie knew already what the decision would be; but consciously she kept insisting to herself, "I'm not going to give all this up for Lee! He deserves it!" Coming to Newagen at dusk was coming home, though the house was dank and empty, with cobwebs and dead flies in every corner. But the sound of the sea sang in their thirsty ears and the smell of pine wood was spicy in the round potbellied stove.

They inspected the big cellar hole of "Avalon," the new house that Mrs. Kreuger was building beside The Snuggery. The slowness of the Maine carpenters irked her exceedingly, but to Lee it seemed a fine thing that a house should grow with sure dignity like an oak; that there was one place in the rush of the modern world where men took time to build on a solid foundation. He and Myrtie visited with "Bubs" Gray in his store, incidentally acquiring a few groceries for supper. They fried ham and country eggs on top of the potbellied stove in the living room, which they did not dare let go out. They were happy together as up in their chinaberry tree; and yet there was no deluding themselves they were still children. Between them still lay the dark question of what they were to do with the rest of their lives.

"The northern lights are blazing," Lee told Myrtie excitedly. "Let's go down on the cliff a few minutes before we go to bed."

He flung a blanket over Myrtie's shoulders, and drew her along with him, stumbling over the half-seen rocks, to where the sea lay hushed and quiet at their feet. The view was magnificent. Beyond the star-brightened sea shone the home lights on all the little islands, a necklace of brightness; and far above, the whole dome of the heavens was ablaze with glory. Long streamers of rose, yellow, and icy white, sparkling like diamonds, flung themselves from one vast horizon to the other; the Milky Way was a path of splendor, edged by a million flowering stars.

"It makes you feel small, doesn't it?" Lee murmured, awed. "A little pinprick in the vastness of the universe. And yet—you know something? I bet the Lord's more interested in what's become of my Human Fly. . . ."

"Oh, Lee, Lee!" Myrtie gasped, laying her cheek against his. "My darling, you don't have to be bishop! Or secretary of anything! Stay with your Human Flies, if you want to!"

Lee's arm tightened proudly about her and together they looked up at the great blaze of splendor that was merely the footstool of the Lord, their Friend. "You know the first thing I'm going to do when I get up to heaven," Lee asked her, joyously. "I'm going to stand up there beside the Creator and fling out a few stars!"

CHAPTER 13

Except the Lord Build the House

"Except the Lord build the house, they labour in vain that build it." [Psalm 127:1]

MYRTIE DIDN'T REALLY MIND Lee's turning down the executive job that would have taken him from friendly Worcester to Methodist headquarters in New York City; what really gave her nightmares were the old ministers she met at Conference every year. They had to retire at sixty-five on a pension too small to feed a healthy cat, so they must fill in with some other job or starve in silent gentility. The ruling in New England to admit just enough men to fill the available, full-time pulpits still left a number of country parishes like Townsend which could afford only a part-time minister's salary; and for these tiny stipends the students and superannuated ministers fought politely but desperately, every spring at Conference time.

It was small wonder that one theological student told Lee and Myrtie in announcing his engagement to a Boston girl from a family of wealth, "Fortunately it's just as easy to love a rich girl as a poor one!"

But the old men wrung Myrtie's heart. Every spring they

would haunt the Conference corridors, carefully dressed in their Sunday greening, broadcloth coats from which all the nap had worn, their thin white hair plastered to look as thick as possible, above their stiffly smiling, anxious faces. They brought their lunches in paper bags to eat surreptitiously in the men's room unless—oh glorious thought!—someone asked them out to lunch. And in each one of them Myrtie saw Lee and herself unless some miracle happened.

It was this specter which helped Myrtie to accept with blind thankfulness what Mrs. Kreuger had done for them in building Avalon and in fixing up The Snuggery so that Myrtie and Lee could rent the smaller house in summer, then retire into the larger one in the winter of their old age. This arrangement would be an answer to an unspoken prayer. Mrs. Kreuger, occupied from morning to night with plasterers, paperers, movers, and with getting the furniture from the storehouse settled, was happier that summer than Myrtie had ever seen her.

The view from Avalon, "crowned with summer sea," was beautiful beyond belief. Set so close to the shore that the sea could whisper or roar in every room, its wide veranda was still so protected you could sit out comfortably on the foggiest of days. Inside, the house was plastered and boasted a furnace so that it would be snugly warm in all kinds of weather, any time of year. The huge living room, designed to be ample for Newagen gatherings, had a vast stone fireplace above which Mrs. Kreuger had commissioned an artist to paint on a great slab of wood the words Susie had written about this friendly house.

> *"We will build you high on the rock of our love*
> *And girdle with peace your beams.*
> *Joy will laugh through your window wide . . .*
> *God bless the dear house of our dreams."*

The jingle expressed the way the Nies family all felt the day we moved into the new home that was to shelter Myrtie and Lee in their old age and to serve as a home of the spirit for all who wished to come there. At first Myrtie was a little worried that Avalon might overawe the villagers so that they might not come to see Lee as readily as they had to the threadbare Snuggery with its cracked ceilings. But she reckoned without the sturdy independence of the New Englander, who not only insists upon managing his own affairs, but grants you that same right. Once having accepted Myrtie and Lee as their friends, the Newagen people did not care if they sat around on crackerboxes to talk, as they frequently had to do at Snuggery when there was a crowd, or sank into Mrs. Kreuger's comfortable chairs.

Newagen had its own standards by which to judge, which suited them perfectly. One morning when Hite Moore came to deliver a mackerel, Myrtie took him through the house; showed him the four upstairs bedrooms, the comfortable suite of rooms for Mrs. Kreuger and her sister-in-law with its own private veranda where they could retreat from the family confusion; the big dining room and kitchen downstairs. Hite said never a word until they paused in front of the large print of one of Rosa Bonheur's paintings where several cows grazed in a gentle landscape. Hite shifted his tobacco from one thin cheek to the other and spoke at last. "The nigh cow looks a good milker!"

But Lee had an uneasy feeling that something was lacking. The Newagenites came as before, but there never seemed to be time to sit quietly on the veranda listening to the sea and the wind until some shy fisherman could find the words to tell Lee what was troubling him. There were always so many people about; why, Lee realized with growing dismay, there was no more privacy here than at the parsonage at home! Peace had fled away down the quiet rocks. He sighed and went back into the house where Myrtie was calling for him to go get some clams for supper. How many? Well, there would be twelve at the table, she thought. Oh yes, and would Lee meet the train at Wiscasset? V., Susie's Englishman, was coming on the three o'clock for the week end.

Mrs. Kreuger spent a happy summer, alternating between having her meals brought up on a tray and queening it at the head of the long table in the dining room. But it was not easy to cater to all of Mrs. Kreuger's sudden whims. One morning, only an hour before noon, she decided she must have lobster Newburg for luncheon. What was the use of being at the shore if they ate only

chicken and ham? Myrtie, sighing, knew that the lobstermen
wouldn't be back ashore till they finished hauling their traps, which
might or might not be before Mrs. Kreuger got hungry; but
Myrtie rushed down to consult with Bubs Gray at the store.
"Bubs," she asked anxiously, "can you get me some lobsters for
this noon?"

"Nope," he said. "Too busy." There was no customer but
Myrtie in the store, and Bubs was carefully peeling off a slice of
yellow cheese with his big sharp knife, to munch on. He offered
Myrtie a sliver.

"Thank you. But I must have a couple of lobsters, Bubs," Myrtie
pleaded. "Mrs. Kreuger's set her heart on it."

Bubs regarded her through shrewd, mild eyes, asking lazily,
"You sure you ain't got a tiger by the tail?" Without waiting for
Myrtie to answer, to figure out if he could possibly mean what she
suspected he did, he weakened as every male always did before
Myrtie's wide, candid gaze. "I 'spose I could take a run out to my
lobster car. But it'll cost you something."

"That's wonderful of you!" Myrtie cried, relieved. Bubs kept
his word. The bill delivered with the lobsters read:

5 lbs. lobster	$2.00
Rush	.10
	$2.10

Later Myrtie realized that the village people had seen what
was happening at Avalon long before she did, but at the time she
only laughed, and let the tiny irritation slip from her mind. But
the tenseness of the atmosphere surrounding Mrs. Kreuger was
unmistakable when V. arrived from Boston to visit me for the
week end. V. was a distant cousin of her former husband's whom I
had met at her apartment at dinner, while he was studying at
Harvard. He was shy, reserved, but with a twinkle in his brown
eyes that belied his formality when he clicked his heels and bowed
with Old World charm. I found V. so different from the hail-
fellow-well-met boys whom I knew as to be fascinating. Mrs.
Krueger watched us look at each other down the long dining-

room table that week end and definitely did not approve of what she saw.

"Vivian and Susie are not suited to each other," she announced flatly after V. had left, in an I-want-no-more-of-this-nonsense tone. "She should marry a minister like her father!"

What business was it of hers whom I married? I was about to flare up hotly when I saw Myrtie looking at me anxiously, so I merely left the room. But my cheeks burned at the thought that Mrs. Kreuger would certainly tell V. what she had me, probably with footnotes. And V. hadn't said a word about marriage! Perhaps he had a girl back in England. This thought upset me so that I tossed all night in my comfortable bed, wishing heartily that we were all back in The Snuggery in its old state. The way Mrs. Kreuger had had the place all prettied up for the renters who were to pay the taxes for Avalon, you hardly recognized the carefree home where we children had grown up.

But the next day when Mrs. Kreuger laid the deed to Avalon in Dad's hand, a deed she had had specially drawn up by her lawyer so there would be no question as to Lee's ownership of both houses, I was ashamed of myself. Certainly no one could be more generous, more understanding than she was; how V. and I felt would not depend upon her, anyway. It was our own secret.

Suddenly, one day late in August, Mrs. Kreuger announced at breakfast that she had ordered her chauffeur to bring around her limousine to take her to Boston that afternoon. Myrtie stared at her blankly. "But your apartment will be awfully hot still! Aren't we making you comfortable here?"

The old lady patted Myrtie's shoulders, confessing, "I get restless, staying in one place too long. Besides, I think you should have a little time alone with your own family. Don't fret. I'll be back."

But two weeks went by with still no word from her. Myrtie worried to Lee, "Do you think we could have hurt her feelings in some way? I can't think of a thing, except what she said about Susie and V."

"Don't worry," Lee said sensibly. "She'll get over it."

But the vague uneasiness must have been in his mind, too, for Myrtie saw that he was taking the long way home to Worcester via Boston that September. Mrs. Kreuger was at home in her ornate apartment and was, they found, relieved, very glad to see them. She demanded instant details about how they had left Avalon. Had they remembered to grease everything so it wouldn't rust in the sea air? Was the boat safely out of the water? Had Myrtie remembered to put moth flakes in the Snuggery blankets? She'd bought them in Canada and they were too handsome to be moth food.

"You'd think I was ten," Myrtie sighed, as she and Lee started home in Jehu after a sumptuous dinner that evening. But she remembered to smile at the hotel doorman in such a way that he tucked the robe about her feet tenderly, and shut Jehu's rattly door as grandly as if it had been Mrs. Kreuger's long black limousine. Myrtie's smile was a tip worth working for.

"She hasn't a thing in the world to do but sit on one of her gilt chairs and worry," Lee pointed out. "I don't think all that red wallpaper helps any either; it would drive me into a fever. We must get down oftener to see her this winter."

But that was easier said than done. Trinity had grown so in the past five years under Lee's preaching that it now took more time than ever to get around the parish. Lee found his study desk piled with notes from his secretary telling of sick and troubled people who must be called upon at once; he preached at least three sermons a week; and he would let nothing interfere with his meetings with the children of the parish. He taught first one class and then another, on Sunday mornings; for even if the Sunday school was so well organized as to run itself, Lee wanted each child to feel that the minister was his personal friend, and that the church belonged to him. Dad had no patience with those who felt that children should not be allowed to join the church until they were "able to judge for themselves whether they want to or not."

"Do we let them judge for themselves whether or not they will brush their teeth? If they will learn arithmetic or reading?" he asked.

When one official of the church came to the parsonage all upset because one mother had brought her young son with her to the communion railing, Lee told him the story of Fred who had lived on a sheep ranch in Texas.

Fred was twelve, and his particular job on the ranch that spring was to look after the baby lambs. Every evening at dusk he would drive them and the mother ewes into the corral in order that they might be safe for the night from the prowling coyotes. Fred liked to watch the silly little lambs leaping and skipping about in the sunny meadow; they reminded him of the Lamb of God in the stained-glass window of his church uptown. The minister last week had come into the Sunday school to invite anyone who wanted to join his class for probationary members. Fred had been among the first to say he wished to join the church, but his father objected.

"You're too young yet to know your own mind," he told the boy. "In a few years when you're older, if you still want to join, it's all right with me. But not now. You don't know what you're doing."

Fred argued hotly that he knew exactly what he was doing, but his father was adamant. That night at dusk Fred went out to the corral as usual, but the family had barely sat down to supper when a terrific racket broke out under the open window, with the lambs yelling their heads off and the ewes blatting anxiously back.

"What the devil's going on out there?" the father asked angrily.

Fred looked at his father. "I left the lambs outside the corral for tonight," he announced calmly. "They're too young to know if they want to go inside where they're safe or not."

"Needless to say, when the District Superintendent gave the new church members the right hand of fellowship, Fred was there," Lee ended, his eyes twinkling. "Young folks will be welcome at the Lord's table as long as I am minister at Trinity."

In addition to his church duties, Lee had become involved in so many community projects that the days were too short to keep all his engagements. The superintendent of the Worcester District wrote in his report to the New England Conference that year, "No minister in the city has a larger place in the hearts of Worcester people than has pastor L. A. Nies." This was partly true because Lee came more often to learn from his parishioners than to preach.

"Jesus was not ashamed to work with his hands," he used to say. "And he knew his job. The yokes that he made were always easy on the burdened oxen." When Lee called upon a carpenter, he would insist upon being taught how to miter two pieces of smooth wood. If he happened to stop Jehu at a mill owner's mansion, Lee would spend the time discussing the practical economics of how to treat the workmen in a Christian manner and still make money for both labor and the investors. Or maybe when a beaming housewife served him tea, he would demand the recipe of her spice cake to take home to Myrtie. Whatever he learned Lee was apt to mention next Sunday in his sermon.

"A man can live his religion in every nail he hammers, in every letter he writes, in every golf ball he hits with a clean, hard stroke," Lee insisted. "A Sunday Christian is so lukewarm that the Lord promises to spew him out of his mouth."

Although the war was over, Lee found that much of the wreckage of people's lives remained to be patched up. One of the most unusual problems that came to his parsonage door was that of Margaret Sullivan and John Hammerface, a full-blooded Indian. Lee heard him coughing and looked out the window to see the two of them coming up the steep parsonage walk to the front door, with the man leaning hard upon the arm of the sturdy Irish girl.

"We want to be married right off," the girl told Lee after he'd rushed out to help her with the sick man and had settled him into a comfortable chair in the front parlor. She opened her bright-red patent-leather bag, drew out a paper, and handed it to Lee. It was their marriage license, with a five-day waiver. She explained, "We haven't very much time to be together. The doctor gives Johnny only a couple of months."

Lee stared bewildered at the healthy, rosy-cheeked girl and then at the man who was obviously in the last stage of tuberculosis. He hadn't any business marrying anyone! What could the girl be thinking of? Probably he had a pension from the war. . . . Was she one of those harpies who wanted to go on milking the government? "I'm sorry. I couldn't possibly marry you," Lee told them firmly. He asked the girl, curious, "You're a

Roman Catholic, aren't you? Why don't you go to the priest?"
She nodded. "The priest won't marry us either. But I've got
to take Johnny home with me! I want to take care of him and
I can't unless we're legally married. Please, please let us tell you
what happened to Johnny before you say no."

Johnny Hammerface, the Indian, had been drafted from
Michigan and had served two years as a sharpshooter in France.
He gasped, his breathing like tearing silk, "They gave me a
telescopic sight, so I shot seventy German officers. Their shiny
buttons glittered so in the sun I couldn't miss. It was just plain
murder." He had hated everything about the war, leaving his
home where he had been brought up, crossing the cold and
turbulent sea, killing endlessly; but worst of all, Johnny was
lonesome. When the mail came, there was never any for him. He
knew they hated to write, but his folks had gone to school; they
could have answered just one of the many letters he sent off day
after day, asking about the red mare, if his sister had had her
baby yet. But no word came. Johnny was gassed in France and
spent long months in the hospital; but as soon as he could, he
rushed back home to Michigan, to find everyone well and all his
letters unopened in a trunk!

"They just didn't care," Johnny Hammerface told Lee bitterly.
"None of my own people cared if I lived or died. I guess I went
kind of crazy. I left home, and took a ticket on a train going anywhere. I got drunk. I got sick again. Finally I got off the train at
Worcester and went into the restaurant for a cup of coffee."
When he smiled at Mary, his face lighted up so you would never
have known he was the same man. He gasped, "Mary was there."

"I'm a waitress," Mary explained proudly. "Johnny told me
about himself. He came back again and again to eat. We got
acquainted." She leaped to her feet, and Lee rose too, so that
they faced each other as she cried, "I want to give him back a little
of what the war took from him, Mr. Nies. I know what you're
thinking. But I don't want his pension. All I want is Johnny! I
want to take him home with me. I don't want him to die alone, in
a hospital. I love Johnny and he belongs to me!"

"Bless you," Lee said slowly. "I'll marry you, Mary."

A Methodist marrying a Roman Catholic to an Indian! "Was I right or wrong?" Lee asked his friends at the Clerical Club next Monday. "What do you fellows think?"

The Clerical Club, which met in Boston every Monday, the ebb tide of a minister after his hard Sunday, was a closely knit group of clergymen whom Lee loved; he would as soon have missed his sermon as his Clerics. Each week a member presented a paper upon some theological subject, which the other members ruthlessly attacked; but the real meat of the occasion came when the Clerics dawdled over luncheon to swap stories about their queer parishioners. They teased Lee now, and said probably his wedding ceremony wouldn't take, but was better than letting the two of them live together in sin. Their hilarity was a safety valve from the strain of their daily living. Burdened as they were by the almost unbearable weight of sin and suffering that came to their parsonage doors, they found in these real-life stories a sort of confessional in reverse, where the priest told all frankly, and was shrived by laughter.

Lee's story about Effie's marriage and her young son David brought down the house one Monday morning.

Effie, a young unmarried mother of seventeen, had spent a term at the Framingham Reformatory for Women before Myrtie took her in at the parsonage to help with the housework. Effie brought her baby, David, with her, a plump, rosy, handsome child as so many "love children" are. The whole Nies family were willing slaves to David; but when Dad was making his sermon, it was Susie's weekly job to amuse the baby so he wouldn't cry. Often she played the old Edison gramophone softly in the kitchen, for Effie loved the squeaky gay records as much as David did; in fact, as Lee told Myrtie privately, there was very little difference, in his opinion, between her mental age and the baby's. What on earth was to become of Effie when they had to send her away from the parsonage, as of course they would when the move to the next parish came?

The answer came knocking on the parsonage front door, asking to see Effie. Beaming, she introduced the hefty young man as David's father! He stayed all day playing with David, getting in Effie's way when she tried to sweep; he came next week and the next. Finally Lee suggested, "Why don't you two get married, and take care of David together?"

"My job doesn't pay enough for me to buy a new shirt and get married too," the groom demurred.

"I'll make you a wedding present of three shirts," Myrtie offered, for Effie had told her the wage the lad was making, which was ample to care for the three of them. "And you can have a couple of Lee's old ones. You needn't pay any wedding fee, either. That always comes to the minister's wife, you know"—she smiled at Lee—"so I can remit it if I like."

Effie was radiant in her new dress the day of the wedding. The living room was filled with flowers and the old gramophone was on the table where Susie was to play the record of the wedding march. At last we were all arranged to Effie's satisfaction, the groom in his new shirt beside the bride, Lee in his long black clerical gown, Myrtie as witness, and Susie at the gramophone. The wedding march started gaily, "Squeak, squeak, Edison Record, tum, tum, ti tum. . . ."

"Stop!" cried Effie suddenly. "Hold everything!"

"What's the matter?" Myrtie gasped.

"I forgot David!" explained the bride. "Run right up to my room and get him, will you, Susie? He'd never forgive me when he grows up, if he wasn't invited to his own mother's wedding!"

After the good fellowship of the Clerical Club, Lee went over to the hotel to call on Mrs. Kreuger but found she was away in Florida. It was strange she hadn't told you she was going, for usually she kept you posted on all her trips. Myrtie must write, ask her up to Worcester to dinner, as soon as she came back.

But there was small time for formal dinner parties that spring because Lee and Myrtie had to move again, leaving his beloved Trinity family to go to Somerville. The ugly, big, old brick church surrounded by clanging streetcars was to be sold, as was Grace Church; and with the resulting funds a great stone cathedral was to be built farther out near the suburbs where most of the two congregations now lived. The new church would be called Wesley.

"Naturally, Wesley will have to have a new unbiased minister," Lee explained to the dismayed Myrtie to whom the years in Worcester had flown by like so many happy days. "A younger man, maybe."

"Don't you dare say you're old, Lee Nies!" Myrtie flared. "Because that would make me old too, and I won't be!" Her eyes brimmed with mischief as she added, "I notice you're not too doddery for peroxide blondes in blue veils to tag around after you."

The red ran up Lee's neck to his ears and his forehead. "Did that widow lady come here to the house? I asked my secretary to get rid of her. She's a pest. But how can I refuse to see her when she insists she's so worried?"

"Worried about how to get a man," Myrtie sniffed. "But I got rid of her. I told her how you snored." When Lee opened his mouth in horrified protest, she chuckled. "Well, if that isn't the truth, exactly, neither is that female's golden hair!"

The Somerville parsonage was adequately furnished already, so that Myrtie had some difficulty fitting in what Lee called her "orphans." The squirrel instinct was strong in Myrtie; she never could bring herself to leave behind anything when she moved. The big Worcester attic had been full of near-antiques, wobbly chairs and tables people had given her which Myrtie assured them Lee would fix better than new in his spare time. But with 1400-odd parishioners, Lee's spare time was purely hypothetical, so the tables still staggered and the chairs wobbled when they arrived at Somerville.

I gave up my room where I was living in Boston and came home to Somerville just in time to hang up "the horribles," as I privately called them. "Aurora, the Rosy-fingered Dawn" was a four-foot canvass with a six-inch gold frame, which took up nearly one whole living-room wall; facing this was a cheap lithograph of St. Mark's, Venice, with pigeons rampant; on the third wall hung two adenoidish babies, awake and asleep, labeled "Morning" and "Night," which Myrtie had acquired with green stamps; while the fourth and worst horrible showed several feeble-minded kittens playing at blocks.

"But, darling, that's Currier and Ives!" Myrtie protested, horrified, when I suggested hanging this behind the piano.

"When I get married, I'm going to live in a modern house shaped like an egg," I announced dreamily. "All glass, so the pictures are outside."

"What about taking a bath, darling?" Myrtie inquired.

"Well, anyway, I won't marry a minister," I protested. "Will you please try to see that the choir quartet aren't practicing in our living room when V. comes to see Dad tonight?"

"Oh. I thought he was coming to see you." Myrtie smiled at me so lovingly I rushed up to my room and burst into excited tears. Why on earth did V. have to ask Dad if he could marry me? It might be an old English custom, but this was the U.S.A., 1924.

We were still digging dinner plates out of barrels when V. arrived, so supper was late. It was also a typical parsonage meal; the telephone rang several times before dessert, which was peaches out of a can; a member of the parsonage committee dropped by to see if we needed any new pots or pans; and finally Dad had to rush off to visit a woman who, as her daughter explained apologetically over the phone, thought she was dying, but probably it was just something she ate. V. kept muttering to me under his breath, "Most extraordin'ry! Is it always like this?" The first view of a parsonage is often a bit unnerving to one not brought up in its hysterical tempo. The only way V. could have asked Dad for his daughter's hand in the good old English way was to use a loud speaker or to follow him to a deathbed. I don't think V. ever did ask Dad, in so many words.

But a wedding rates higher than an engagement any day; and this was a big year for love interest in the Nies family. Dad went out to Ohio to marry Ike to Lillian, a classmate of his at Ohio Wesleyan University where Ike had transferred for his last two years of college. The bride and groom, instead of settling in Cleveland with her folks or in New England with Ike's, compromised in New York City where Ike had lined up a salesman's job; a job he was eminently fitted for, as he had his father's friendly charm.

"Lee Nies, do you realize that in nine months I could be a

grandmother!" Myrtie wailed, aghast. Then her face cleared. "But
grandchildren are much more fun than your own, everyone says;
you can let their parents do the spanking while you do the
spoiling!"

Ike and Lillian wrote ruefully that they couldn't afford to come
home that Christmas; they needed furniture, and so many
things. . . . Myrtie had written to invite Mrs. Kreuger, as usual,
for Christmas dinner, but the letter, after much wandering, came
back to Somerville; and when Myrtie called the hotel in Boston,
the desk clerk explained that Mrs. Kreuger was traveling again in
the South, going from place to place, so it was hard to reach her.
So there were only four of us, Dad, Mother, V., who was now
considered a member of the family, and I to take off the fruit of
the big Christmas tree in the front parlor. (The Sunday school
always gave the minister theirs after the party at the church, but
the tree was always so huge you had to edge your way among
the branches in the parsonage parlor.)

"It's kind of fun, just the family lolling around in our bathrobes,
opening presents," Myrtie yawned happily, beaming at a frivolous
negligee Ike and Lillian had sent. The sound of feet pounding up
the front steps outside made her lift her head, listening.

Lee looked guilty. "I forgot to tell you, dear; I invited the
Greens and their three children to dinner. They're new in the
church and their family's way out in Iowa, so I thought . . ."

Myrtie wailed, "But there's only one duck, and not much meat
on ducks anyway!" The doorbell rang as she gathered herself
together for quick action. "V., run down cellar and get that jar
of deer meat the lighthouse keeper's wife at Cuckolds gave me
last summer; we can cut the duck meat off the bones, mix 'em, and
make a big pie, and no one'll know the difference. Susie, wrap up
that perfume Ma Rouse sent me for Mrs. Green and put it on the
Christmas tree. And wrap that pound of candy into three paper
napkins for the children. Lee, for goodness' sake answer the
doorbell! Merry Christmas, everybody!" She drew herself up
in her old bathrobe so that it looked like a gay hostess gown
especially donned for the occasion. "How very nice of you to
help us celebrate Christmas, you dear Greens!"

I have often wondered whether, if V. and I had eloped quietly instead of announcing our engagement, having a formal wedding, the storm with Mrs. Kreuger might not have been averted; but Dad always said comfortingly that a hurricane that had been building up as long as this one had could hardly be turned aside.

In any case, two days after my engagement picture appeared in a staid Boston newspaper, the unbelievable letter arrived from Mrs. Kreuger at the Somerville parsonage. Actually it was signed by her lawyer, demanding in acid legal shibboleths that both Avalon and Snuggery "which said Mrs. Kreuger had been forced to finance under false pretenses," be given back to her! Lee read the letter twice, his hands cold and shaking, before he handed it over to Myrtie to see if it possibly meant what he thought it did.

"She's gone crazy, Lee!" Myrtie gasped, white-faced and horrified. "She must have lost her mind. Snuggery's *ours!* It's our *home* and always has been. And we didn't ask her to build Avalon. What can be the matter with her?"

"I'm going right in town to see," Lee said grimly, reaching for his hat.

Mrs. Kreuger must have known he would come, for she'd left word at the hotel desk that she was not at home to Mr. Nies. A blow in the face could not have slapped Lee more quickly into realizing the frightening reality of the situation. His hands fumbling with Jehu's gears as he started back home felt numb and awkward, as if they didn't belong to him. Mrs. Kreuger must really have argued herself into believing what the lawyer had said! She must have sat there in her red-walled room, in a fever because she couldn't make each member of the Nies family bow to her inflexible will, plotting new methods of making us come to heel, until the announcement of V.'s and Susie's engagement wrote finis to her hopes of domination. Action she must have of one kind or another, so now she would fling herself into a crusade of tearing down the good-will edifice she had so carefully built up. In her heart she must know this incredible patchwork of evil intent she had put together wasn't real. How could she trade all the laughter and sunlight at Newagen—all her planning for the village people, for Lee's retirement—for lonely venom? Suddenly, seeing things from her point of view, Lee was sorry for her.

"It must be terrible to think that all everyone wants of you is your money," he told Myrtie with something like horror when he got home, and held her in his arms until she stopped shaking with nerves. "Poor, lonesome old soul."

"She'll sue, all right," Myrtie predicted, shivering again. "You wait and see."

"Let's let her have the whole thing," Lee suggested.

"Snuggery?" Myrtie gasped. "But Lee, it's the only home we have! Avalon, yes. She can have that. But I'm not going to give up Snuggery to anyone!" She burst into loud sobs and refused to be comforted till Lee promised he wouldn't ask the impossible of her.

Lee went to see Mrs. Kreuger's lawyer and came home looking sick. He told Myrtie, "Now I know what Chris Crane felt. Perhaps this is good experience for me." But Myrtie snapped, "Don't be ridiculous"; Lee hadn't stolen anything, nor had he even wanted anything that wasn't his. Besides, she pointed out, giving back both Avalon and Snuggery as Mrs. Kreuger demanded would be a tacit admission of guilt, of intent to victimize an old lady, when you knew this to be absurd. It would start a whispering campaign in the Conference which they would never get away from. Much cleaner and better to stand up and fight for their good name. They argued back and forth half the night before they slept the sleep of exhaustion.

In the long uneasy weeks that followed, Lee tried to think the unhappy situation through honestly. That there had been no intent on his or Myrtie's part to defraud was without question; but could anything they had done have *looked* as if they had been trying to deceive Mrs. Kreuger? Certainly he and Myrtie had been as naïve as a couple of children, accepting every toy offered them. But that was the usual way the minister was paid, partly in salary and partly in donations from the parish; he took what was given him in the free spirit in which it was offered.

Those pound parties at Townsend had saved their lives almost literally, when he and Myrtie were trying to make ends meet on $520 a year! The first time Myrtie had seen the church people come crowding in the front door of the parsonage bearing a pound of home-made butter, tea, coffee, succulent apple pies, canned vegetables, and meat, cakes groaning with rich frosting, she had burst into humiliated tears.

"But, Lee, it's just charity," she wailed, when he drew her upstairs to his study to find out what was the matter.

"Listen to the fun they're having." Lee soothed, smoothing back her soft, tumbled curls. From the kitchen below they could hear shouts of laughter, and the pungency of boiling coffee was delicious. "It's a social event, sugar. Don't take it too seriously; it's just a good old country custom. Besides, they'll eat up most of the cake and stuff before they go."

But the crumbs of implication the pound parties had left behind were not good, Lee admitted to himself, looking back. Not good either for the church people, whose consciences were soothed for paying such niggardly wages to the parson, or for the minister who would be less than human not to wonder how soon the next supplement to his salary would come. More serious, how much extra help a preacher got depended more upon his personal charm, how popular he was in the village, than upon his integrity, his independence of thought, which alone made for real leadership in the pulpit.

In all his life, Lee could reassure himself, he had never catered to or fawned upon his wealthy parishioners; most of them would have hated this as much as Lee would have. But never, even at Trinity, had Lee been given a salary adequate to cover both his family's needs and the entertainment required of him as head of a big business, the church. The parsonage was not looked upon merely as his home to which he could invite his personal friends and leave out those who were not congenial; the parsonage door had to be open to everyone; it was treated as an annex to the church which had to be kept scoured, scrubbed, and ready for every emergency—at the minister's wife's expense. Myrtie thought nothing of entertaining fifty to a hundred church ladies at tea; even though the other women helped out with the food, this was expensive, with flowers, silver, tea, and coffee. A cleaning woman or a maid was not a luxury but a necessity if Myrtie was not to be back in bed sick. When the Epworth League met at the parsonage, Myrtie furnished coffee and doughnuts; and the choir's aching void had to be filled after their annual parsonage rehearsal. The list was endless. Not to mention the hundreds of troubled people who came to see Lee and whom Myrtie comforted with "a nice hot cup of tea" and the official church visitors, ministers, missionaries, district superintendents, bishops, who expected as their right to spend the night, at least, at the parsonage.

"Perhaps a minister should have an entertainment account, like a traveling salesman," Lee speculated. "Maybe then he could balance his budget."

But balancing his budget was only part of the problem, Lee saw; the real crux of the matter was that no minister should ever accept a personal gift, however badly he might need it. For to do so sapped his independence. Therein lay his own weakness, Lee saw, if not his sin. But what would he have done, if friends had not helped him during Myrtie's sickness, paid for her nurse and medicines, sent Lee himself on the trip to Bermuda that saved his reason? "The Lord sent us all these good things with His love," Myrtie had assured her good friends gratefully. But now Lee wondered why it had occurred to nobody to raise his salary to an amount adequate for his needs and then to let him stay within these limits, like any other salaried man? *The gifts should be to the church, not to the minister. If the laborer was worthy of his hire, the salary should be adequate and impersonal.* In gifts, however generous, the seeds dangerous to the person's self-respect and to his independence were buried deep, but they were there.

But none of this shutting-the-door-after-the-horse-was-stolen philosophizing settled the matter of the letters Mrs. Kreuger's lawyers kept on sending, keeping the Somerville parsonage in a constant state of tension. Lee finally went to a lawyer friend to ask his advice. The friend advised Lee to let the matter come to trial in court. "You have the deeds to both houses, Lee," his lawyer friend pointed out. "You have letters to show why Mrs. Kreuger built Avalon as a place for you and Myrtie to retire; you have the dates of all the many church and social meetings you have already held there at Newagen. Goodness, man, you can't lose! From what you tell me, this right-about-face is nothing new for her anyway. She's done it with members of her own family at one time or another. You could win this case hands down."

"But the church would lose," Lee pointed out heavily. "Think of all the publicity! Can't you see the headlines? MINISTER ALLEGED SWINDLER." Lee gathered up his papers and thrust them into his already sagging blue coat pockets, insisting, "I've given the church thirty years of my life. I'm not going to disgrace it now. Not even for Snuggery, which is our home." In this decision he could not be shaken.

"At least before you send her back the deeds—and that would be a crime against Myrtie, Lee, believe me—give me a little time to talk to Mrs. Kreuger's lawyer," his friend begged. "Maybe I can make him see sense and settle this out of court, at any rate."

Lee wished later he had not agreed, for the indecision was harrowing. Try as he would to ignore the whole thing, thoughts crept out of the corners of his mind as he lay upon his study couch to rest, and wrote themselves across the page when he was typing his sermon. It would be better to give up every rock and blade of grass at Newagen than to have your mind poisoned with uncertainty.

Nor could Lee help a crawling feeling under his skin whenever he went to Methodist headquarters in Boston. Did he only imagine that people stopped talking abruptly as he came up? Or was someone too cordial out of pity, feeling, "There, but for the grace of God, go I"? That all the Conference members knew about Mrs. Kreuger's accusations he was certain. For the first time in his life he was self-conscious when he met his friends, watching for the slightest hint of recoil. He talked things over with his bishop, who was satisfied that Lee had done nothing to embarrass the church; nevertheless Lee had an uneasy suspicion that anyone with Mrs. Kreuger's wealth and determination could bring a great deal of pressure to bear in high places. He was soon to have proof of this.

"Hello, Lee, you old horse thief!" a hearty voice called one morning at Methodist headquarters. Lee's face lighted up. "Fred!"

Bishop Fred Fisher had been a classmate at theological school. Freshly back from India, he was intent upon raising money for new dormitories and schools, he explained to Lee. He eyed his old friend curiously, demanding, "What's eating that old woman in the hotel down the street? She sent for me to come over there like an errand boy, and I went because I hoped she'd hand me a dormitory or two. Instead she lit into me about *you*. Said you'd stolen a couple of houses from her or something. I just reached for my hat. 'If you're talking about Lee Nies, that's a lie,' I told her. 'I've known him since we were in school together and he isn't capable of stealing. He happens to be a friend of mine still. Good morning, Madame.' And I walked out on her. But what do you mean, costing me a dormitory?"

Lee couldn't speak, but his eyes were suddenly luminous as they were when they were happy. Ironically he came home that night to find that the date of his court appearance had been set; but Lee's lawyer friend said not to worry; he was sure the disagreement could still be settled before then. But what if it wasn't? Lee worried. He paced his study floor most of that night.

Lee was determined that nothing should spoil V.'s and his Susie's wedding. As the date approached, the sinking feeling in my own stomach got worse, for I knew how Mrs. Kreuger must be foaming at all the newspaper reports of parties, of the coming ceremony at the Boston University School of Theology chapel. Would Mrs. Kreuger go so far as to protest my marrying her husband's cousin at the ceremony? I wondered, shivering. Night after night I would dream that V. and I were standing in front of the altar while the minister asked if anyone knew any reason why we should not become man and wife, and Mrs. Kreuger's voice would cry, "Stop!" I would wake up in a cold sweat. Once I must have cried out in my dream, for Dad came into my room in his dressing gown, sat down on the edge of my bed, and reached for my icy hand. He didn't ask what I'd been dreaming; I think he knew. He just sat there quietly until I slid off into sleep.

I was frantically unpacking presents the day before the wedding when Lee slid rather guiltily into the living room with two orange tickets in his hand. "They're playing Beethoven's Fifth this afternoon," he murmured, "at Symphony. Let's get out of this mess. Just this last time, we'll go alone." His eyes added, "Things will never be quite the same between us again; you'll belong first to someone else. This great music will find words big enough for this thing between us. I love you very much, my dear."

We sat shamelessly holding hands while the music of the great master who heard only with the listening ear of the soul surged and swelled to majesty about us. (All of my days when I hear Beethoven's Fifth, I shall feel cherished, protected, secure in my father's love in whatever world he may be.) When we were rattling home in Jehu, Dad gave me my real wedding present.

"What are you crying for, silly?" Lee asked tenderly. "To whom would the family silver go, except to my eldest child?"

He'd laid in my hand a silver quarter. It was not the one his father had given him, he said; that had been spent long ago. But this silver still bore the insignia of a great country and great words to live by: "Liberty" on one side and on the other "In God we trust." This silver coin had become our family coat of arms, the precious heirloom to be handed down to our children.

Mrs. Kreuger made no nightmare appearance at the wedding; everything went off beautifully, although I was too tired to care. After V. and I were gone on our honeymoon, Lee found little time to worry about his own problems. He had his whole parish to take care of.

One afternoon when Lee got home he found Myrtie pacing his study floor. "I want to go up to Newagen!" she told Lee, her eyes flashing. "I want to go home to Snuggery. I want to sniff the sea air and watch the ocean that doesn't care who's good or who's bad. Darn it, Lee, I will too swear!" she cried and then she laughed. "Remember how Ike used to say when he was little, '*I need to be bad!*' You know something, Lee? Last summer Bubs Gray asked me if I hadn't gotten a tiger by the tail! He knew how Mrs. Kreuger felt even then."

"Bubs is a wise old man," Lee admitted. "He must be pushing

eighty now. . . . Wasn't that the postman?" He came back, tearing open an envelope with his lawyer's name on it; his eyes
devoured the message before he passed the letter to Myrtie,
wordless. An agreement had been reached with Mrs. Krueger's
lawyer, Lee's friend wrote, whereby she would take over both
Snuggery and Avalon; but in return she would give Lee enough
money to buy another small cottage at Newagen if he wanted to.
This amounted to a tacit admission that she had not been coerced,
Lee's lawyer pointed out, if Myrtie and Lee would be satisfied
with that.

"Satisfied!" Lee shouted, whirling Myrtie round and round his
study. "We'll shoot right up to Newagen to look for another
place, sugar!"

Myrtie swallowed, her face still long. "What right has she to
take *our home?* I don't want another. . . ." Lee kissed her and
began to haul out a suitcase for their night clothes. "Pack a lunch,
will you?" he asked. "It'll be late when we get there. No, we'll
stay at some rooming house so we can start to look for our new
place right after breakfast."

The cottage they found was half a mile from Cape Newagen;
it was small, perched like a sentinel gull upon the high yellow
cliff, with a magnificent bird's-eye view along the curving, rocky
coast. But the little house had many drawbacks; it had been built
by a minister who was no architect and who had learned his car-
pentering as he went along, so that the bedrooms were mere slits
with walls so thin, as Myrtie said, you could hear anyone change
his mind. The kitchen was so small the leaky icebox had to sit
upon the back veranda; the hot-water heater smoked, and a neighbor dropped by with the cheerful tidings that the fireplace hearth
had fallen into the cellar last week when trodden upon by a possible purchaser.

"It can all be fixed," Lee argued, his eyes upon the beautiful
curve of the pine-crested shore out the window.

"But the sea doesn't *sing* here. We're too high up," Myrtie
mourned. What she meant was that it wasn't Snuggery, hushed
close to the waves; it wasn't home.

"The children will come here, and the grandchildren," Lee assured her. "We'll sing again, louder than ever with all that gang. Let's stay the night and see how it feels."

"The beds look lumpy," Myrtie said doubtfully, "and there isn't a thing in this place to eat."

"Someone's knocking at the back door!" Lee said and went to investigate. It was one of the village women carrying a blueberry pie still hot from the oven. She said shyly, "Bubs said you ain't laid in any provisions yet, so I just dodged up with this."

A few moments later there was a second knock. "Ma sent up this clam muddle," a ten-year-old boy in dungarees mumbled and fled down the path like a scared chipmunk. A third knock proved to be the gift of a pan of fresh bread and a dish of newly churned butter; no, the neighbor from the Cape wouldn't come in; she'd just run up here before she set out her own folk's supper.

"It's a welcome home, Lee!" Myrtie cried. "They believe in us anyway. Oh, Lee!" She flung herself down upon a lumpy iron cot and cried and cried; but Lee wisely left her alone, knowing the loving thought of their Newagen friends had opened up the too-long-stoppered bottle of her grief. Finally Myrtie sat up and wiped her eyes. "There, that's crossed off," she said briskly. She came over to where Lee was standing by the window and slid her arm through his. Together they watched the yellow finger of the Cuckolds Light sweep through the gathering dusk and brighten the gray face of the sea.

CHAPTER 14

What Is Success?

LEE WAS MADE SUPERINTENDENT of the Springfield District of the New England Conference in 1925, a vast area that covered 1500 square miles with over sixty parishes, partly large city churches, mostly smaller town and lovely white country churches like Townsend's, to which he was to travel over 14,500 miles in the ancient Jehu, during the coming year. He had now completed the cycle, he chuckled to Myrtie, from bribing the Presiding Elder with her angel cake to being the V.I.P. for whom other preacher's wives made cake.

"Queer, isn't it? I don't feel a day older," Lee murmured. And Myrtie added she hoped he'd keep to his diet better than the P.E. had. Remember, no sweets; he knew what the doctor had said. Lee went on absently, "The only trouble is, I don't know near as much as I did my first year in Townsend! The only thing of which I grow surer and surer is the love of God." He smiled at his wife, his blue eyes adding wordlessly, "And of yours."

Nevertheless, out of the deep well of his humility and experience, Lee was able to water with a practiced hand the young green sprouts on his widespread district that traveled over the

202

tall hills and far away. He knew exactly what his young ministers were thinking when he walked in to hold the fourth quarterly conference, to listen to yearly reports of collections, growth in membership, parish calls made, and eager additions to the Sunday school. The youngster was wondering, "Is the old crab in a good humor today? Will he give me a good recommend to the bishop? Gosh, I hope Sally has a good supper for us after the meeting!"

Lee did not eat the desserts and he brought his own saccharine for his coffee, but he always praised the "bite to eat" that the minister's wife had been up since daybreak to prepare. Often he asked to look in upon the sleeping preacher's kids, rosy and quiet for once in their tumbled beds, with Lee's hand a silent prayer upon their tousled hair. The district soon learned Lee was as genuinely interested in their family problems as they were.

"You're so late," Myrtie would complain sleepily as he climbed into bed at two in the morning after driving home from a tiny parish far up in the hills.

"You can't find out what's really going on till you get to the second-piece-of-chicken-pie stage," Lee told her wearily. "I knew there was something wrong in that church—collections falling off, attendance low, and yet the boy's a good preacher. I found out tonight the poor guy's worried about his wife; she needs an operation he can't afford. I promised to call the Deaconess Hospital tomorrow—lucky I'm on the Board—and see about getting her a bed. Cute little woman." He yawned mightily and smiled at Myrtie, murmuring, "She reminds me of you."

All the cute little wives reminded him of Myrtie, whether they were dark or blond, and in all of his bright young men he saw himself, starting off eager, scarcely out of the bud, bursting with more green confidence than common sense. But that was the way the world got ahead, Lee thought, by unconsidered leaps, stumbling, maybe even going a step backward, but not going entirely back to the starting point. Progress even in religious experience was a little like the day when you'd climbed Mt. Chocorua in New Hampshire; you started up steeply then went along on the level for a while, then dropped down a little; but in the end, sweating and breathless, you made the peak and looked down on the glory of green swelling fields and incredibly blue lakes spread out before you, with a sort of God's-eye view.

Lee found one young preacher in his district was on the verge of a nervous breakdown because he and the chairman of his official board couldn't see eye to eye. "I try to be tolerant, but he's so granite-minded!" the young man stormed to Lee when he arrived. "Every single time I try to snap this complacent bunch out of the rut, he stymies me by saying, 'But my dear fellow, we don't do things like that in our church!' We need partitions in our main Sunday-school room so the teachers can be heard, but he says that's pampering. I have all I can do not to grab him by his beard and yell, 'So what, you old goat?' " The boy's almost hysterical voice dropped and he looked at Lee anxiously, his lips quivering. "A swell religious leader I turned out to be! Do—do you think I ought to get out of the ministry?"

Lee smiled. "I think you need a change. No one can be a success when he's worn out, exhausted. There's a nice outdoor restaurant about a mile down the road. Come along and have dinner with me."

It wasn't exactly calming for the young man to ride in Jehu with Lee, who disregarded his brakes entirely until they reached the restaurant, but the dinner was excellent. They sat outdoors at a tiny table beside a brook that furnished a muted orchestra, and the lad ate so ravenously of the fried chicken that Lee wondered if he and his wife were getting enough to eat. You'd have to have a word with the chairman of the official board before you left town. Finally, when the coffee came, the young preacher leaned back in his chair with a sigh of pure content, his eyes on the setting sun flinging crimson banners across the evening sky.

"You were talking about being successful, Mr. Nies. Just what do you call 'success'?" he murmured.

Lee looked at his young sprout. How much was he capable of understanding? Advice to most young people mostly went in and out one ear; they had to learn the hard way. But maybe a few ideas would percolate. "Success isn't just making money," Lee said slowly. "It's the number and kind of satisfactions you get. Some men find satisfaction in heading up an organization; others get it in making a better bathtub or toothbrush. But it is the creators, the poets, scientists who do pure research, the artists, and the statesmen who rise above mere politics who achieve lasting success; and into this group falls the minister. To my mind, his is the greatest job in the world because it deals with creative personality."

"I see what you mean," the young minister agreed. "It's no use building bigger and speedier airplanes to zoom through space, unless we know where we're going."

"Unless we know some place worth going to," Lee corrected. "The man who sets up the ideals of any nation or group of people *controls that nation.* You can be clean without bathtubs; but you cannot live fully in every sinew and fiber of your physical, mental, and spiritual being without an ideal bigger than you are. In plainer words, without God."

"But ministers make mistakes like anyone else, Mr. Nies," the boy admitted ruefully. "Probably I shouldn't have been so hotheaded with my old goat—" he grinned apologetically, "—respected chairman of the official board."

Lee grinned back. "Probably not. Surely the minister makes mistakes, but his emphasis is in the right place. He keeps doggedly coming back to begin again. One of his greatest satisfactions— which *is* success—is in helping people whose ideals have cracked to glue them back together again. Let me tell you a story that happened when I was about your age."

The cashier of a small-town bank near his first parish had absconded with all the bank's funds and fled to Canada, Lee related. The minister of his church had followed the cashier, urging him to come back to face restitution and jail, and the cashier had returned, penitent but penniless, all he stole having been spent for gambling debts. But his family paid more heavily for the banker's mistake than did the man himself serving his sentence at state prison. When Lee saw a golden-haired little girl crossing the Common one morning and asked who she was, someone answered scornfully, "Oh, that's a jailbird's brat! Her father wrecked our bank. There's hardly a family in town that didn't lose something. Just wait till that guy gets out of jail; he won't dare live in this town again."

But this is exactly what his minister persuaded this man to do. "If you don't lick this mistake of yours right here, it'll follow you all your life, wherever you go," the minister promised earnestly. "You're lucky that your wife has stood by you. And so will I. I'll get you a job and I'll meet you at the jail door."

But when the minister and the too pale ex-banker got off the train at his home town, an angry crowd was waiting. Someone yelled, "Here comes that bum. Let's get him, fellers!" The man's wife and little girl who were waiting on the station platform drew back in terror, but the minister stood quietly beside his friend. The crowd, muttering but unwilling to attack the minister, slunk away one by one as a mob usually does when they have to face a man unafraid to stand up for what he believes. The ex-banker went into chicken farming, built up a good business. Finally one Sunday morning when his little girl joined the church, her father stood beside her and joined too. And there wasn't a member of the congregation who didn't shake hands with him afterward and mean their warm welcome back to the house of God.

Lee looked at the boy across the table and ended quietly. "That, I think, was success. Not only for the ex-banker but for the minister. For in helping others to grow, he stretches his own personality." Lee looked at the sunset fading rapidly into violet and knew he must soon be on his way to that other church he must inspect this night. But he couldn't quite bring himself to leave. He murmured, "Some people make collections of snuff boxes and leave them behind to museums. Other men build big businesses that are their monument. Once in a lifetime, maybe, a man writes a great poem in which he speaks God's thoughts after him, in living, flaming words for men to cherish. But the minister who gave that thief back his heritage as a son of God—can there be a greater satisfaction than that?"

When Lee saw his young minister surreptitiously wrap up his sugared pecan roll in a paper napkin to take home to his wife, he was certain that the chairman of that official board needed talking to. He dropped the boy preacher at his neat white parsonage and then stopped by the chairman's office. Lee listened to the older man say patronizingly that their new little minister had some good ideas, but they were too costly for his church to afford. Why should they pay for individual Sunday-school rooms when their fathers had always made themselves heard over the chatter by yelling a little louder?"

"How much do you pay for liquor and entertainment every month?" Lee hazarded abruptly, glancing at the other man's florid face.

"Why, fifty dollars maybe," the other man faltered astonished.

"How much does your minister get weekly?"

"Why, the same, fifty dollars."

"How much is your annual pledge to the church?" Lee continued directly.

"I don't see what business it is of yours." The other man squirmed, flushed, finally admitted, "Fifty-two dollars. I give a dollar a Sunday."

"You spend more in a month for your own pleasure than you give in a year for your Lord's work," Lee pointed out. "And you, the chairman of the church board, say you can't afford partitions for the Sunday school!" Lee got up, started to leave. "Do you know that your young minister tithes his fifty dollars a week? Do you?" He walked out of the office of the now speechless businessman without looking back. A month later Lee received a jubilant letter from his young preacher saying that not only were they going to fix up the Sunday-school room but his own salary had been raised. He ended piously, "God moves in a mysterious way. . . ."

"Humph," said Myrtie, who'd heard all about the incident. "Not so terribly mysterious. How much did you give that youngster, Lee?"

Lee grinned. "Only fifty dollars, sugar."

Lee couldn't help thinking more and more about his young minister's query, "What is success?" This was like asking "What is truth?" when each was such a relative thing. Success for a Hottentot in Africa sticking a root into the fertile ground to sprout without further cultivation might be different from that of a Kansas farmer harvesting with his wheat combine; but the principal ends would be the same: satisfaction of the farmer's need to eat, of his pride to hold up his head among his neighbors. And even greater satisfaction was in helping someone else to reap his harvest of the spirit, for there the results might be not only temporal but eternal.

"We are a part of a great procession," Lee told himself dreamily. "It is the minister's mortal immortality, to coin a paradox, that he can start so many children marching toward creative living. Who will preach for me when my tongue is stilled? Well, there's Elsa whom I got the college scholarship for; she's teaching now in the Philippines. Then Ken . . . those primary schools he set up in our mission at Montevideo were so good the government is copying them for their own schools. Ina is teaching chemistry at Yenching . . ." He sighed. It would have been nice if either Susie or Ike had felt drawn toward preaching but since they hadn't . . . Lee brightened. Maybe the new baby would be a minister some day!

Perry Lee, named for both grandfathers, was born in Cleveland on a March day to Ike and Lillian Nies. Susie, who went on from Detroit where she and V. were living, reported to Lee and Myrtie that Perry Lee was the smartest baby she'd ever seen. He even cried intelligently—and got what he wanted. "You did that too," Myrtie wrote Ike. "Your dad and I will be out to spoil the baby as soon as we can." Myrtie kept her word so happily that much as they loved her, Ike and Lillian could not help a sense of relief when Jehu rattled away from Ohio. A few years later the second grandchild was named Evelyn Sue after Ike's and Lillian's sisters. Ike telegraphed the new daughter's weight in ounces to the waiting Nies family "Because every ounce of her is so dear." The third and last grandchild was V. and Susie's contribution; he weighed less than five pounds but he had a grand name.

"We've got General Richard Montgomery in the family at last!" Myrtie exulted when she learned the new grandson's name was to be Richard. That this was also an old family name in V.'s heritage which dated back to Richard the Lion-hearted did not change at all his grandmother's announcement that the baby was named for the general whose direct descendant it was impossible for little Rick to be—legitimately.

Lee worked on the Springfield district for six years; the last, 1929, was, as he wrote in his annual report to the Conference, "the most successful in spite of flood and flu, which have laid many of our people low." A Crusade for Christ in which he had enrolled all his churches over the big sprawling district had resulted in 1200 new members and an increase in their giving to both home and foreign missions.

Traveling about so much, speaking night after night at special meetings, had taken such a toll of Lee's strength that one night the accident happened which Myrtie had dreaded in secret for so long; Lee fell asleep at Jehu's wheel and woke up in the hospital when they were picking pieces of the windshield out of his face. The doctors let him go next morning, for they could find no traces of internal injuries; but they were there all the same, waiting to appear. With her uncanny intuition where Lee was concerned, Myrtie suspected this and insisted from then on upon accompanying Lee wherever he went, whether to quarterly conferences where she stayed outside in the car and read or crocheted, or nights when he went to speak. But she did her best to camouflage her anxiety.

"We'll stop at all those exciting little antique shops along the road," she planned happily.

"Oh bum." Lee swore his worst swearword, groaning, "I'll be nothing but a traveling junkman from now on."

Myrtie made up in enthusiasm what she lacked in knowledge. Jehu was piled high with "Sandwich glass" made in Ohio; with paintless old benches, crocks, and what Lee called "yellow stuff with warts." But he grudgingly tied on the back bumper an old sea chest with brass corners which was really good and a blanket chest with the smell of sandalwood inside. What did it matter if they were antiques or junk, if Myrtie was happy?

"It's like collecting pieces of people's lives," she told Lee dreamily. "I bet some girl got that luster pitcher for a wedding present. And that funeral urn with the flowers around it has real hair in it."

"You paid out my good money for a hank of hair from someone you never even knew?" Lee groaned.

"That's going to buy you a new pulpit suit, young man," Myrtie assured him. She slid her hand inside his. "Thirty years is such a short time to be married, isn't it?"

Was it the accident that made Lee walk so slowly lately? If anything happened to Lee. . . . A hand closed about her throat, making it hard to breathe.

That spring Lee had the fun of transferring to a bigger parish the young man whom he had taken to dinner beside the brook; and this time at Conference, the young preacher took Lee to lunch. They got to talking about the new million-dollar Trinity Church, a vast Gothic structure that had been built in Springfield not far from Lee and Myrtie's district parsonage. They worshiped at Trinity on the infrequent Sundays when Lee was not preaching. One of the wealthy manufacturers in the congregation had built a lovely stone chapel for use for weddings, christenings, any occasion when the cathedral church was too big.

"I dropped by Grace Chapel the other day," Lee told the younger minister. "It was empty but the sunlight flooding through the windows threw a crown of red and blue jewels on the gray stone floor and there was such a sense of peace. . . . It was as if the chapel were praying without words. I heard the sound of a door closing and looking around me. The man who'd paid thousands to build this chapel was on his knees in the back pew; he'd come in for a moment's silent worship too. He looked tired. I knew, with the depression on, that his business had been having hard sledding."

"So I asked him," continued Lee, "Don't you wish now you had back the cash that this building cost?" He smiled, "Oh no, Mr. Nies. This is the best investment I ever made, for no one can take it away from me. And it pays dividends every day!"

The young minister looked across the luncheon table, repeating what Lee had told him months ago. "And that, I think, is success."

But in spite of the way in which his district was booming, Lee felt no exultation; he was tired, so very, very tired since his accident that often he had to fight to stay awake at meetings, which wasn't like him at all. He stopped eating, nibbling only at his favorite dishes which Myrtie anxiously prepared. The night he fainted at a quarterly conference Myrtie, backed up by the doctor, laid down the law, "We're going down to Newagen to rest. Of course the new cottage won't be like Snuggery, but I can feed you up, and the air there is better than medicine." She got a friend to drive them down to Maine; and because Lee, unwound at last from his tensions, found the quarter-mile walk to the village store to swap yarns with Bubs Gray and his cronies too much to manage, his Newagen friends came to him. They would saunter up to the back door of the cottage, their big sea boots silent upon the mossy path, and stand there until Myrtie happened to notice them.

"Why, Eben, come in," Myrtie would cry. "How long have you been standing out there? Why didn't you knock?"

"I was afraid Mr. Nies'd be sleeping, if I heaved out a yell," Eben would explain, hauling out a couple of lobsters from a newspaper parcel. Or perhaps he'd bring a quart of blueberries he'd picked. "Could you use these, Mrs. Nies?" Myrtie would make a pie and insist upon Eben staying to help eat it. Or maybe Hite Moore would "dodge up with a mackerel Mr. Nies might fancy," and stay to supper too. Afterward, they would all sit around the crackling fire in the great stone fireplace which Lee had had built in the front wall of the new cottage, with windows on either side so that you could watch both the fire and the sea at the same time. But significantly this new house had no name; it was just "The Cottage." Outside of the cosy room the gray fog would creep by and the voice of Carrie, the foghorn at the Cuckolds Light, which Lee always insisted blew in the key of G major, would cry to all ships groping their way off the rocky coast, "Beware!" But inside would be warmth and good laughter.

"Did I ever tell you about Cap'n Pringle's false teeth?" Hite asked one evening as they were toasting themselves about the fire. When Lee answered, "No, why?" the other man's lean sunburnt face crinkled into a silent chuckle. Cap'n Pringle, he explained, was snugger'n the bark off a tree. Hite had been deckhand on the ferry on which the old man used to haul summer people around the islands, so he knew how tight the cap'n could be. Cap'n Pringle didn't have no more teeth'n a hen; so one day when he was up to Portland, he bought himself a new crockery set. But the ready-made teeth didn't fit very well, and when he wrote back to say so, the Portland dentist said to come back and get them refitted.

" 'Tain't nuthin' but a trick to git more money," Cap'n Pringle allowed. He looked across the supper table at his housekeeper, Liz, who was soaking her toast in her tea because she didn't have a tooth in her head either. The cap'n tossed his store pair across to her, ordering, "Here, Liz. You break 'em in for me."

Liz hadn't been able to chew good for fifteen years, so now she sure made hay. She fixed herself up steak and onions, big smokin' hunks of roast beef, and all the good vittles she'd had to leave go so long; while Cap'n Pringle had to set acrost the table from her and watch, his own mouth watering with envy. Finally he could stand it no longer. One day he made Liz give him back his teeth, yelling angrily, "I'm going to heave 'em overboard. If I can't use 'em, you can't neither!"

Here Hite paused in his story, chewed reflectively on his tobacco for a few minutes, eying Lee and Myrtie sitting there by the fire; when Hite was sure they were worked up to the proper pitch of curiosity he ended solemnly, "They tell me, come fall, when they was haulin' out to Monhegan, they hauled up a big lobster usin' Cap'n Pringle's teeth to chaw his way out'n the trap!"

Such laughter did Lee more good than much doctoring, Myrtie knew; and she was vastly relieved when Lee was able to get down to the Cape again; he even insisted upon preaching one Sunday morning at the schoolhouse. The windows were open and when an inquisitive cow put her head inside and mooed, Lee didn't crack a smile. "One at a time, sister," he urged. After a month at his beloved Newagen, Lee went back to his district "twice as good as new," he insisted; Myrtie was the only one who knew this wasn't so: how white Lee was when he came home at midnight after a long day. But there was nothing she could do about it except watch carefully to save him all the steps possible. She knew it was useless to ask him to slow down the pace he had set himself, both day and night; Lee simply didn't know how and he wasn't apt to learn at this late date. Besides his district duties, he carried on his heart all the people he had helped in all his former parishes;

they were as dear to him as his own family. One of these was
Angela P.

One afternoon Lee came home from Clerical Club to find Myrtie
in their room, reading a letter and crying heartily. He gathered
her up in his arms, demanding, "What's wrong, sugar? Not Snuggery again?"

"No. It's Angela," Myrtie wept. "She's dead and now she'll
never see little Angie and her new baby! The baby's due any day
now and I was going to—" She looked up at Lee, freed herself
from his arms, and said almost defiantly, "I was going to send
Angela her own grandchild's picture! After all, I didn't promise
about the second generation!"

Lee and Myrtie had never quite agreed about the best way to
handle Angela's tragedy. To Lee a promise was a promise and
sacred; Myrtie believed this too in principle, but there were times
when her heart spoke so loudly it was hard to hear her conscience.
Still, Lee knew, she had never told Angela where her baby had
gone; only that she was well and happy.

Angela was a nurse, lovely in her white uniform, with her great
dark eyes, her softly waving dark hair, and her gentle mouth; if
there was one word to describe her it was "lady"—perhaps
"generous lady" is more accurate, for Angela never did anything
by halves. When she fell in love with the handsome state policeman in his smart blue uniform whom she met near the hospital,
Angela went all the way. Unfortunately when she found she was
going to have his child, her lover had to tell her that he already
was married. Angela, like the prodigal son, "came to herself" with
a great sense of shock; but unfortunately she had no father to go
home to. In Italy she had relatives, but not here.

Angela refused the father's offer of money proudly, and when
she could no longer work, went to stay with a nurse friend in
whose home the baby was born—little Angie. She was a beautiful
child, with her father's dark-gold hair and her mother's great
brown eyes and sensitive mouth. It was like tearing her heart to
leave the baby, but Angela had to go back to work. She boarded
little Angie from place to place, but as the little girl grew older,

there were other problems. Little Angie had asked why she had
no daddy like the other children. "Will she hate me when she
knows she's illegitimate?" Angela grew cold just thinking of this
inevitable day. Once she came to visit her child unexpectedly and
was horrified to hear her scolding her pet puppy with lurid oaths.
"Where did you hear that?" Angela gasped.

"Mr. Smith says it when his truck won't start," little Angie said.

The next day Angela went to Lee to ask him to help her find
a new boarding place for her baby. Lee looked at her and said
gently, "Angela, you don't want a new place. It's just begging the
question. I have a suggestion. I know a family in one of my former
parishes who have just lost a little girl exactly the same age as
little Angie. They want to adopt another little girl, give her the
dead child's name, and raise her as their own."

"You mean let them adopt little Angie?" Angela gasped, horrified. "Oh, I couldn't! She's all I have!"

Lee looked at her, hating to say what he must and yet knowing
the hard way was the only one, for the child's sake. "Those other
people can give her everything," he pointed out. "They'll teach
her hymns instead of swearwords; they have plenty of means;
they can send her to college if she's bright enough to go. And they
can give her also—" Lee hesitated, then plunged in his surgeon's
knife cleanly as he ended, "They can give her a father's name to
be proud of when she goes to school with the other children."

Angela was white to the lips. "I—I suppose I could see her once
in a while?"

Lee shook his head. According to the state law, if she gave little
Angie up for adoption, she'd never even know where she was, or
her new name. It was a hard law but a good one, for the child
would know no wrangling, no tearing apart of her affections
when she grew older. "Just think it over, Angela," Lee urged.
"You can let me know what you decide."

"No!" Angela got to her feet, stood holding onto Lee's study
desk as if she'd have fallen without it. "If I do this for little Angie,
I've got to make a clean break *right now*. I couldn't bear to think
about it." She was trembling but she lifted her dark eyes to look
straight into Lee's, asking, "It's a question if I love her more than I

love myself, isn't it? All right. Go ahead and fix up the adoption papers. I'll sign them."

She never saw her baby again or knew her new name. Myrtie and Lee had had to promise the state adoption authorities they would never tell what they knew; but Myrtie was burned up with pity for Angela. She promised, "Maybe I can't tell you where little Angie is, but I'll keep in touch with her, and make sure she's all right. I can promise you that, Angela dear."

During the next fifteen years, Angela had followed Lee and Myrtie around from parsonage to parsonage, wherever they were sent. She never asked in so many words about her baby, but she'd just sit there in the front parlor, waiting like a starving man for any crumbs of information Myrtie might drop. For she had kept her word; she'd been often to see little Angie, whose new name was Marie. "She's doing fine in school," Myrtie'd tell little Angie's mother. "She just won the spelling bee in the third grade!" Or later, "Little Angie's taking piano lessons. She can play 'The Blue Danube Waltz.'" Angela wouldn't say a word, but her dark eyes would shine and her whole face grow proud. Once Myrtie cut off the signature at the end of a little scrawled note Marie had sent, thanking Myrtie for a Christmas present, and gave the letter to Angela. Angela stared at the big childish writing, opened her bag, put the letter from her child inside, and rushed out of the front parlor.

"It's heartbreaking the way she grieves," Myrtie told Lee. "But what more can I do?"

"Nothing," Lee said. "But she has her children in the ward at the hospital. Dr. J. tells me she's so good with them that when a child's very sick, they always send for Angela."

Lee went to the hospital to visit, and Angela was telling a story to the whole children's ward while she gave baths. The beds were all full and everyone was forgetting how much he ached to listen to Angela's story about the little pig who got hurt but never squealed when he had his face washed. That child with the pert upturned nose must be Irish, Lee thought; and the thin little one was handsome enough to be Italian; while the cute little colored girl whom Angela was bathing had dark little pigtails sticking out every which way, each one tied with a bright-red ribbon. When she heard Lee's footsteps Angela turned so fast she almost upset the basin of bath water, and Lee knew, seeing the wild hope in her eyes, what Angela was hoping and yet was afraid of too. She thought that maybe sometime the child to be brought in here might be little Angie.

"But she must know that Marie is sixteen now!" Myrtie protested. "I declare, Lee, sometimes I wonder if we did the right thing. Angela's never married. Would it do any harm, do you think, if I told Marie, the next time I see her, what a wonderful mother she really has? She'll be proud."

But Marie flared up at Myrtie. Proud of a mother who'd loved her so little she'd walked out on her, had given her away? In spite of Myrtie's shocked protests, Marie refused flatly to listen to a word about her mother, and that was that.

"Marie's adolescent," Lee comforted Myrtie, who had meant so well. "Now she's shocked at not being like the rest of the gang. She'll grow up." Myrtie was so unhappy that she sent Angela Marie's graduation picture when she finished high school. When Lee was doubtful if this was best, Myrtie snapped, "Just imagine if I'd missed seventeen years of Susie!"

This was all that Angela ever had of her baby, a scrawled little note and a stiff picture of a thin girl with eyes too big for her face, in a white dress. Marie went to college, met a boy there she loved, and they were married; but Marie's own mother wasn't invited. Shortly before Marie's first baby was born, Angela died very suddenly in her suite at the hospital where she was now superintendent. "There didn't seem to be much wrong with her," the puzzled doctor told Lee. "She just didn't want to live."

Myrtie sobbed after the funeral, "It seems just terrible that Angela didn't even know she was going to have a grandchild! She'd have been so happy. I think. . . ." She hesitated and looked up at Lee, and he knew she was up to something but he decided perhaps he'd better not know what it was. Often Myrtie's hunches proved more right than his considered actions. Myrtie decided things in her heart, rather then in her head. She took to haunting the mail slot in the front hall and for weeks was upset and irritable. She'd snatch up the mail from the floor when the postman thrust it through, run through the envelopes, and then her face would fall.

"You'd better tell me what's the matter, sugar," Lee said finally.

"If you must know, I wrote to Marie all about her mother!" Myrtie confessed, her cheeks blazing. "I told her just how wonderful she was! I told her her mother's and her own name too had been Angela and it was a name to be proud of. Oh, Lee, maybe I shouldn't have written. Maybe she'll hate me for it and never answer. I'm such a fool." She flung herself into his waiting arms and he told her he liked the kind of fool she was, and not to worry. One morning a small white envelope fell through the mail slot onto the floor and Myrtie pounced upon it. She tore open the envelope and ran with it up the stairs to Lee's study, crying and laughing at the same time, she was so happy. "Marie's named her new baby *Angela!* She understands now. She loves her mother. Oh, Lee, if only Angela knew!"

"I think maybe she does," Lee consoled Myrtie. "Have you forgotten the Lord's a Father, too?"

It was partly because of this that Lee wrote yearningly in his annual report that year, "Somewhere in God's good time, we shall see the day when, in spite of indifference and opposition, this old world will be truly Christian." Statistics and new members and money in the church account at the bank weren't nearly so important as one girl who'd found her way back to loving her own mother. But the incident set him to wanting again a church of his own. As he'd pointed out to Myrtie, organization was not what he wanted; even as District Superintendent he yearned for the priest's job of suffering through with his own people, of keeping alight the flame of service on his own church altar. Lee's peculiar genius for this pastoral job was pointed up by what he did in bringing Tom Gandy back to life when, to all intents and purposes, his days were ended.

"Lee, did you read the morning paper yet?" the minister of Trinity Church phoned him one morning. "You know Tom Gandy?"

"Sure. He gave me the cash to buy an organ for a little church up in C—— last month," Lee said. "Anything wrong?"

"Everything's wrong. His partner just absconded with all the firm's assets," the minister replied. "Tom's as honest as daylight, as you know. The first he knew about it was when the district attorney called him. I went over there, but Tom wouldn't see me. His wife says Tom's half out of his mind; but she thinks maybe he'd see you."

"I'm on my way," Lee said, dropping the receiver and reaching for his hat. The shades were down on all the windows of the big brick Gandy house, Lee saw when he got out of Jehu, as if there'd been a death. When Lee rang the doorbell, Tom's wife opened the door herself, and Lee was shocked. Could this be the confident woman in the gay little hat and fur coat who'd laughed up at you last Sunday morning at church? Her hair was pinned up carelessly and there was even a spot on the front of her crumpled house dress. "It's a mercy the children aren't home," she was saying nervously as she ushered Lee into the dim house. "Tom says we'll have to take them out of college. He says we'll have to sell this house, though it's in my name. I don't mind that but . . ." Her eyes filled with tears as she motioned toward the closed doors of the library. "He's in there," she said. "I—I think he's losing his mind."

At first the room was so dark Lee couldn't see, and then he made out Tom sitting there in the big armchair. His thick dark hair had gone completely white in one night and his eyes were staring at the wall opposite him. He didn't answer when Lee spoke to him, so Lee drew up a chair and sat down, keeping silent company. How long he sat there with this shocked, stricken man Lee never knew, but it was dark when he came out of the library. He'd laid his hand on Tom's before he went, saying, "I'm coming back, Tom. I have a little business to do tonight. But I'll be back in the morning." Tom didn't flicker an eyelash, but somehow Lee knew that he'd heard.

Lee was gone from home till after midnight. At first Myrtie didn't worry; but it got to be ten, eleven, twelve, and still no Lee. Had he fallen asleep again? Had another accident? Her heart leaped with relief when she heard Jehu rattle into the garage, but she saw at once that Lee was too tired to tell her where he'd been. So she merely fed him the chicken soup she'd been keeping hot on the back of the stove and tucked him warmly into bed. He was

asleep before she got into her own twin bed. And next morning
when she woke up, Lee was gone again. The sun was just slanting
bright rays in the kitchen window when he came home, and Lee's
face was another glory.

"Where have you been?" Myrtie cried. "I've been so worried!"

"I've been to Tom Gandy's," Lee told her. "I knew he wouldn't
want to wait to know. I went to his chief creditors last night and
they've all agreed to wait till he can pay them back. Tom was still
sitting there alone in the library when I went back. Did I tell you
his hair had turned white? I told him how all his creditors believed
he was honest. I told him, 'Your friends at the church believe in
you too, Tom. You know what they've done? *They've arranged
to go on your note at the bank so you can borrow what you need to
start your business again.*' "

Tom lifted his newly white head, and then, as the words got
through to him, his eyes came slowly to life. He gasped, "You
mean—they'd—do that—for me?"

"We'll go down to the bank together," Lee promised. "Just
as soon as it opens. You may have lost your money, Tom, but you
haven't lost your good name."

Telling Myrtie about it, Lee's voice faltered and tears glistened
in his eyes. He knew now what Lazarus had looked like when
he walked from the grave of his living death.

"But, Lee, is he really going to start his business again?" Myrtie
demanded. "What did Tom say?"

"He didn't say anything to me," Lee told her, rubbing his hand
over his tired forehead and then through his thinning hair. "He
was down on his knees thanking Almighty God, so I just tiptoed
out and left them together."

CHAPTER 15

Our Conversation Is in Heaven

"*For our conversation is in heaven; from whence also we look for the Saviour, the Lord Jesus Christ.*" [Phil. 3:20]

MYRTIE HAD ALWAYS HOPED that when their time came, she and Lee would "go together." An automobile accident, maybe? She used to think about it when she woke too early in the morning and lay in that relaxed state which is neither waking nor sleeping but a little of both; when it is too late to change yesterday and too early for today. But it made you think these days when you met your friends almost as often in the obituary columns of the newspaper as on the street. It didn't seem possible you and Lee had passed the sixty mark! The way he drove Jehu, when he had his mind on his sermon, hurtling down those narrow mountain roads—Myrtie shuddered.

Do you really foresee things before they happen, or do they occur that way because your mind has already laid down the pattern? she was to wonder a few weeks later. She and Lee were hurrying to make one of his speaking engagements on time when Jehu hit the tidewater bridge crossing the Merrimack River too hard, swerved, crashed through the guard railing, and hung there with the front car wheels poised over the abyss. When Myrtie looked out her front window, all she could see down below was the hungry river.

"Don't move, sugar," Lee cautioned calmly. As if you could, when the bottom had fallen out of your stomach and the queer, paralyzing copper taste of fear was in your mouth. "The least jar might send us over. I think Jehu's rear wheels must have caught on something."

You'd thought you were ready to die but you weren't, Myrtie knew, numbly, scarcely daring to breathe, listening to the excited buzzing of the crowd gathering behind them on the bridge. Someone had called the fire department which came, roaring and clanging, but then crept up on the bridge very quietly, afraid to loosen the frail hold of Jehu's wheels. Myrtie said, trying to keep her teeth from chattering, "Well, at least we're going together."

"Going where?" Lee snapped. "Not till after my speech tonight in Lynn. I'm too busy to drown." It was so exactly like him that Myrtie chuckled, sliding her hand into his; and they sat there chatting quietly while the grappling hooks the firemen had fastened to Jehu's rear end drew them, inch by cautious inch, back to safety. Lee made his speaking engagement, but not in Jehu. As they rushed along in the hired taxi, Myrtie decided on some less harrowing way of exiting together from this world below.

But she forgot all her worries in the excitement of moving back home to Townsend. "I'd like to end my ministry where it began," Lee told the bishop. Sixty-five was retirement age in the New England Conference, but you could still hold a part-time job if there were any left over. Queer, wasn't it? Just when you were beginning to get an inkling of what living was about, they scrapped you as "too old." "I was happier in Townsend when I was a boy then anyone has a right to be. I had the job I wanted, the woman I wanted, and my first child was born there in a prune box!" Lee chuckled to the bishop. "If I could go back in the retired relationship. . . ."

"We're really old! We're retired!" Myrtie thought numbly as she sat there in the big conference room, hearing someone else appointed to move into their former parsonage. Into all their parsonages except Townsend, bless the bishop! Was Lee really old? She looked anxiously at him sitting there beside her; his hair was getting a trifle thin but his black Sunday pulpit coat wasn't green yet around the edges. "I'll sell my antiques to buy him a new suit," she planned.

So they wrapped the scarred piano legs for the last time, and after forty years, went back to Lee's "little crooked lovely hills" and to their friends and their friends' children. "I knew everyone at the post office this morning!" Lee reported gaily when he went for the mail the first day across the spring green of the Common with its wooden stand for the band concerts on summer evenings, its friendly white houses facing each other across the grass; while on the far side, up on its hill among the pines, the shabby white of the Christopher Wren tower on the old church rose in wooden music to the blue sky.

"The only thing retired about this job is the salary," Myrtie grumbled ruefully when Lee preached twice on Sundays, taught a Sunday-school class, organized a young people's group, and called every afternoon on villagers, or rode Jehu over the crooked hills to the outlying farmhouses. But she knew perfectly well he couldn't stop; the pattern of his ministry had become his breath of life. It did not even occur to Lee he could take things easier, and sleep later of a morning. When one of those dizzy spells that had irritated him lately came on, he simply drew Jehu up by the side of the road and waited until the spell had passed.

His Epworth League, the high-school young people, had discussion groups and picnics. Lee liked nothing better than to fill up his big old car with a hooting, laughing crowd in dungarees and sweat shirts, with food and ginger ale bottles dripping out of the luggage compartment, and to ride up into the hills for a "sunset supper." For, queerly, he found that, in spite of their strange jargon of slang, he and these clear-eyed youngsters spoke the same language; they were real, not a pretense in a carload.

"They're immortality," Lee told Myrtie when she protested he had no business climbing mountains and eating hot dogs at his age. "They're the only way you can pass on what you've learned all these years—the boiled-down sap of your experience."

"Hunh," Myrtie countered. "You expect them to listen?"

Sometimes he did wish they'd wear a few more clothes. When Myrtie went bathing at their age, she'd worn a dark-blue bathing suit with a sailor collar trimmed with white, rickrack braid, and long black stockings that met her bloomers. "Mom says this bathing suit isn't decent," one girl laughed to Lee when he'd taken them all swimming in Jehu to the state park one afternoon. She lay there, sprawled upon the grass, wearing very brief dark-blue shorts and a red bra. "But I tell her, 'Everybody's made alike so what does it matter?' "

Their minds were as naked as their bodies, with no meat on them but lovely bones, Lee thought. "Well, I don't think you're deceiving anybody," he admitted wryly. But after all, he thought, watching her shoot from the diving board, an arrow frothing the dark-brown pool, she did really swim, not just jump up and down like the bloomer-encumbered Myrtie used to do. "Being a realist" they called talking about their bodies, hauling out their subconscious to take it apart before anyone who would listen; which, to you, was rather like picking your teeth in a public restaurant. How were you going to make them understand that the things of the spirit were as real as—well, as Cokes, batting averages, and heavy dates? That being born unto the Lord was not some occult psychological experience but as natural as having a baby? And as rewarding?

A wet rubber ball bounced off Lee's ear and he leaped to join the wet, yelling mob. The water, when he dived, shocked the heat from his tired body and left him gasping, but he had breath enough left to duck the skinny young ringleader until he yelled "Uncle!" Lee was still a big man, and he had always been a powerful swimmer; but now a sharp pain shot through his side. Something he'd eaten, no doubt; it would pass. It did, but Lee was glad when the young people decided it was time to leave the park. He lay down heavily on his study couch when he got home and slept so deeply that Myrtie had difficulty waking him for dinner.

"You look flushed." Myrtie was worried, as she felt his forehead for fever.

"It's only sunburn," Lee said crossly, shaking off her hand.

But his head still felt queer, far-off, as if it didn't belong to him. By morning, however, he felt fine and was glad he hadn't let Myrtie make a fuss.

The spring hills were a glory now, delicate with millions of apple blossoms and fragrant with sensuous lilacs and the clean green smell of new hay growing in the sun. And then summer followed the promise of those few unseasonably hot days and everything that grew seemed to leap into a riot of color, scent, and shade. Just being alive, a part of all this fierce tide of loveliness that covered the hills as he drove around his scattered parish, was a daily wonder, Lee thought. As he clattered in Jehu over the winding dusty roads, he tried to sift out in his mind the golden sediment from his sixty-odd years to offer as reality to his bright, naked young people. To offer them the truth as he saw it—but what was truth? There it was again, the old, old query which had bothered him when he was only a young greening in his first little chapel in Dallas. Was truth something that changed styles with the years like bathing suits? Were these youngsters right or were their parents? Or both?

He stopped Jehu one day and got out to walk a way beside the little Squanicook River, a brown-velvet ribbon winding through the long green hair of the grass, and paused to watch a hummingbird drinking from the bright-orange blossoms of a trumpet vine that blazed over an old stone wall, mute evidence that down behind there, in the depression, had once stood a home. The tiny bird, its wings going so fast you couldn't see them, would balance itself in the air in front of a blossom, take aim, plunge its tiny tubular beak into the flower, suck up the honey, then circle and go on to the next blossom; always in exactly the same performance. Fascinated, Lee sat down, leaning back against the gray stone wall to watch.

"There's a law," Lee decided. "And when the hummingbird follows the rules, he gets the nectar. Otherwise he would not." Suddenly, watching the hummingbird, he saw the simple thing which had baffled him so long come clear in the sunlight. "Truth is God's plan for the universe," he saw, exultantly. "So long as we follow it, we are successful; when we lose sight of it, we are lost. The law may seem to change merely because we ourselves are growing in comprehension. A six-months-old baby cannot understand what Einstein can."

Lee moved too quickly and the hummingbird, startled, flew away in a whirr of bright wings. If you sat very still, perhaps he'd come back. The hummingbird's instinct was to fear anything that moved. Were animals, birds, happier than men because they must follow the law of the universe, willy-nilly, while man had not only his inherited instincts but his power to choose what he would do with them? The will to follow God's plan was man's tool of advance. It was like plugging in a radio; the radio might be there and the electric outlet, but only when you connected the two by an effort of will could you hear music from half across the world. You didn't even have to understand the theory of sound waves; you merely followed the plan, and a man spoke companionably in your ear across an ocean. When you tuned in on God's plan for you, then indeed you found power! You could swing centuries on their hinges as Paul had, and Martin Luther, and Abraham Lincoln. Yes, and your own father too had helped to push the world along the way it must go; all the little men pushing together, believing in their own rights as children of God.

The hummingbird was back! Lee didn't dare move a muscle as the tiny, jeweled body hesitated near his left ear, decided he was some new kind of stone, and boldly plunged its beak into the orange-colored blossom just over his head. The tiny bird was so near Lee could see the glistening feathers on its rainbow body. So small it was, and yet so sure of its destiny, what it must do.

"If I could understand you, you lovely thing, I would know what God is," Lee told it silently. "The whole plan."

The hummingbird darted to another blossom; the golden sun of the hot afternoon was like a friendly hand on Lee's shoulders as he leaned back against the gray stone wall; and the scent of the trumpet vine was delicate and sweet. As his eyes closed drowsily, Lee had the queer certainty that the hummingbird's wings were trying to tell him something, singing him a song, over and over, which, if only he could understand the words, would be the key to everything; but though he heard the tune, he couldn't quite make out the meaning. Just as he almost caught it, as so often happened these days, he fell asleep.

He woke with the queer pain back in his side, so bad this time he could hardly stagger as far as Jehu, drive home, and get up to his bed. When Myrtie called him for supper, he felt himself a drowning man pushing up through dark waters. He dropped back, and stared dazed at Myrtie's alarmed face looking down at him.

"Lee Nies, I'm going to call the doctor!"

"No!" Lee begged. "If you do, I won't see him."

You were just growing old, but you couldn't say that to Myrtie, because then she would be old too and that mustn't happen. She must stay young, beautiful, the toast of Fort Worth, Texas. "Don't worry. I'm fine." With a great effort he got up, and kissed her throat where it had begun to wrinkle; but when he smiled down into her eyes, they were as blue as ever and as clear.

One of the nicest evenings he and Myrtie spent together that winter was the banquet at Wesley Church, Worcester, where they both were guests of honor with the other former pastors of Trinity Church which, with Grace, had formed this great congregation. The new stone cathedral, rising majestic upon its hill, was thus partly of Lee's building, and the men and women, looking vaguely familiar, who rushed up to seize his hand had been his children long ago at Trinity.

"Don't you remember my Willy?" a white-haired woman demanded almost indignantly, hustling up a smiling, well-dressed man. "I was mad one day when you came to call on us because I'd found a snake in Willy's bed! And the week before, we'd had to bury all his clothes because he'd been studying skunks. But you said, 'Leave him alone. He's finding things out. He'll be a great scientist someday, and make you proud of him.' Well, I am proud!" She beamed up at her embarrassed son. "Willy's head pathologist up at the state hospital."

Lee's and Willy's eyes met over her head and they both grinned. The scientist murmured, "I wish I had somebody to make 'em 'leave me alone' now. I get so little time to 'find out things.' "

Lee didn't recognize the handsome woman in the low-cut evening gown three seats away from him at the head table, but she was obviously someone of importance, for her eyes and jewels flashed imperiously, and the newspaper reporters kept sidling up behind her chair, begging, "Just one more picture, please?" She stopped by Lee's chair as she swept by, laying an affectionate hand upon his shoulder.

"I'm Linda," she told him. When he looked up at her blankly, she smiled and began to hum.

"Away in a manger, no crib for his bed,
The little Lord Jesus laid down his sweet head. . . ."

The whole table grew still at the sound of that haunting voice that had stopped the curtain at the opera. Lee got up so fast his chair crashed behind him, and he took both her hands. "You sang that for me one Sunday evening! Of course I remember. You were so small I had to stand you up on the pulpit. . . ."

"You put your arm around me to keep me from falling," Linda interrupted. "Do you recall what you said? 'Keep singing, Linda. Someday the whole world will hear your song.' Maybe you don't know my professional name." Lee's eyes widened when she said it, for it was known in opera, radio, in London, Rome, and New York. She went on, "The first time I sang in Paris, I was terrified. I got out on the stage and my throat closed right up; as if adhesive tape had been put over my mouth; and the audience was horrible, grinning at me. Then suddenly I saw another crowd, and I heard your voice saying, 'Keep singing, Linda.' So I did."

Myrtie gasped on the other side of Lee, when the strange, beautiful woman brushed Lee's cheek swiftly with her lovely rouged lips. She asked, "Where are you now, Mr. Nies? Townsend? Wouldn't you like me to come, give a concert for your church? It won't cost a cent. The bill is already paid."

"I'll write you a letter about dates," Lee promised, patting her hand. He wondered a little uneasily how Pagliacci would sound on their organ with the weak bass note. He had no inkling that she would never come; that he himself would have an engagement with another star.

It was Myrtie, sitting beside Lee at the high head table who first spotted the sunflower grin of the Chinese gentleman on the banquet floor who was following Lee's every move with his black eyes. When she pointed him out, Lee rushed down, nearly knocking over an irritated waiter balancing creamed chicken. Lee cried, "Why, Charlie Chin! I thought you were in China!"

"I come back," Mr. Chin beamed. Charlie had been one of the laundrymen in Framingham for whom Lee had started a Chinese Sunday school. At first the Chinese had been more enthusiastic about learning English than in Bible lessons. Because of their language difficulty, each man had had to have his own personal teacher; and Charlie's had been Susie Perry, a worker at the Dennison factory. "I had to leave school early to go to work," Susie apologized when she offered to teach. "But I guess I can read Bible stories to him." But Susie was wise in the ways of God; before the year was out, Charlie Chin had become a Christian.

"I go back to China to have sons," Charlie told Lee earnestly now. "My father is head man in village, but when I tell him, 'I Christian now!' he disown me. 'Go with other foreign devils!' he say. When I go on smiling, he beat me. He does not understand. 'Why you smile?' he ask. I say, 'They beat Jesus, too.' 'Who Jesus?' he say. So I tell him. Finally my mother believe, then my sister, then my father—and so the whole village. We build Christian church, school." Charlie drew a deep breath; it was hard to talk English so long, but he and Lee had years to make up.

"I bring my sons here. I want them to grow up this country," Mr. Chin explained earnestly. "Is great, free country. Great sons."

"Yes," Lee said soberly. "My father felt the same way."

"You come see me?" Charlie begged. "I got ten laundries, here, other cities. I got big restaurant in Worcester. Come, bring your wife. I give you good feed. Everything free."

"Peking duck?" Lee chuckled. "We'll come."

"Peking duck," Charlie promised, his smile nearly meeting at the back of his head.

"You know, that Susie Perry had long fingers," Lee told Myrtie as they climbed wearily into bed that night, too stuffed with food and excitement to sleep. "Imagine a little factory girl reaching clear around the world and changing a whole village in China! And she did it just by being herself. She reminds me of the hummingbird. . . ."

"Lee Nies, that girl weighed over a hundred and fifty!" Myrtie yawned. "Go to sleep. It's almost morning." Suddenly she began to giggle so that she shook the whole bed. "Do you remember the Sunday School concert when the Chinese laundrymen insisted upon singing a song too? They picked their own hymn and we almost died laughing when they began, 'Wash me and I shall be whiter than snow.' "

Next morning when Lee tried to get up, he found the room going round and round in dizzy pinwheels, and the pain was a sword in his side. You'd done too much last night; you'd better take it easy today. He pretended to be still asleep when the telephone rang, but after Myrtie slipped out to answer, she brought his breakfast back on a tray. It was going to be hard to fool Myrtie. He waited cautiously till it was safe to dispose of his breakfast in the bathroom; then he managed to shave, to get on his clothes. Maybe fresh air would help. You could take Jehu, pretend to make some calls, rest by the way. Myrtie mustn't suspect.

"Now, Lee, don't you be late for the Slater girl's wedding," Myrtie cautioned as he left. "They're coming this afternoon at four. I've some roses in the garden for the gray vase, but bring two quarts of ice cream, will you? Vanilla and strawberry, mixed. And don't forget the 'singing birds' like you did at the last wedding. I always feel people aren't really married without that prayer."

In this special prayer Lee kept for weddings, he asked the Lord to bless this new family with sunshine, flowers, and singing birds along their new way, ending, "But if storms must come, may they only draw these thy children closer together." Lee asked suspiciously, "What're you looking at me so queerly for, sugar? I'm all right."

"There's something wrong," Myrtie knew, watching Jehu move off down the street under the tall elms, with unaccustomed slowness. "He's hiding something from me. I ought to have gone with him, but I must straighten up the house for the wedding."

Lee didn't come home for lunch or telephone, and Myrtie's uneasiness grew. At ten minutes of four, when he'd neither arrived nor made any sign, she was in a panic. Had he forgotten the wedding? What were you going to say to them? Oh dear, here they were! Sitting among the stunned, disapproving wedding party, Myrtie went through the agony of waiting, explaining that Lee would be here any second now, smiling with frozen lips while her whole being was listening, tense, for the rattle of Jehu coming into the yard. The squeak of brakes half an eternity later left her faint with relief; but when Lee came slowly into the front parlor his eyes were so heavy, so dazed, that she almost cried out. *Lee was sick. If you made a fuss in front of the wedding party, he'd be furious. Wouldn't this awful wedding ever be over?*

"I was unavoidably detained," Lee was telling the irked bride and groom. "I'm terribly sorry." He avoided Myrtie's eyes. You could hardly explain that you'd been sitting beside the road for hours, afraid to drive for fear you'd hurt someone. Myrtie was right; you'd have to see a doctor; but alone, so you could find out what the score was first.

The telephone ringing as the wedding party left saved Lee from explanations, for it was a wire saying V., Susie, and Rick, their young son, were en route from New York for a visit.

It would be nice, Lee enthused, craftily edging Myrtie away from his own heavy-eyed apathy, having Rick, a little honey-colored head in the spare-room cot bed. (Lee hoped desperately he wouldn't be ill to spoil the visit.)

"I'm going to give Susie the baby pillow Ma embroidered with violets for her when she was a baby, for Rick," Myrtie planned, brightening. "But she must wash it by hand, not put it into the washer, so when Rick grows up and marries, his wife can use it for *their* son." It was nothing for Myrtie to jump thirty years; she barely noticed it. Thank heaven she'd stopped worrying about you, Lee saw thankfully as he dropped cautiously down upon his study couch so it wouldn't creak and warn her. But he couldn't rest after all. A dynamo was screaming in his head and the sunlight streaming through the study window was hot on his face, but he didn't have energy enough to pull down the shade. Did you have a fever? If this turned out to be really serious, what would happen to Myrtie? You weren't afraid of dying; why should you be? But leaving Myrtie behind . . . would Susie take her? Or Ike? She was too independent to be happy in anyone else's home; you could hardly begin after sixty-five years to do things in other people's ways. He sighed heavily, hearing her feet come up the uncarpeted stairs.

"Lee, I hate to bother you," Myrtie began anxiously. "But old Ebenezer Brown is dying and Dr. Reardon says you'd better come."

Dr. Reardon was an ardent Catholic and one of Lee's best friends, for the two of them had watched by too many sick beds to think there was only one path to the Lord's house. Ebenezer, a vigorous man of eighty, boasted that now his white beard had grown so long he didn't have to wear a necktie; and when he approved of something Lee said in prayer meeting, Ebenezer always shouted "Amen!" so loudly that everyone jumped. It was hard to think of him as weak, dying.

As Lee came into the bedroom, the old man was propped up in bed, dressed in his white nightshirt, with his long snowy beard flowing down over the counterpane. "He looks like Moses!" Lee thought. Ebenezer had his big Bible open in front of him, reading, following the words along with his shaking finger.

" 'In my Father's house are many mansions';" the old man read in his whispery voice that was his only sign of weakness. " 'If it were not so, I would have told you.' "

"Can he see to read?" Lee murmured to Dr. Reardon, for Ebenezer had given no sign he saw Lee come into the room.

"No," the doctor whispered back. "It's written in his mind. Eerie, isn't it?"

The old man turned a page carefully and read on. " 'I go to prepare a place for you. . . .' " He paused, lifted his shaggy white head as if he heard someone call him by name. "Why, Eloise!" he said, pleased. Eloise was his daughter, who had died twenty years ago. Ebenezer went on smiling at the afternoon sunlight flooding in his bedroom window, where a ruffled curtain was blowing gently in and out with the breeze. "What a pretty white dress,

dear," old man Brown said. "Wait a minute and I'll be along.
I want to finish this chapter."

When Lee glanced at the window, Dr. Reardon's gaze met his,
and they both looked away sheepishly, for of course there was
nothing to be seen but the white curtain, blowing in and out;
but it was weird, listening to the whispery sound of Ebenezer's
voice reading on and on in the Bible he could not see. " 'And if I
go and prepare a place for you, I will come again, and receive you
unto myself. . . .' " Slowly the book slipped from his fingers;
he sat up in bed and held out his old, shaking arms. A shining came
over his face, a great shining, triumphant joy. He cried, "Jesus!
Oh my Jesus!"

All eternity was there suddenly in that quiet room, chanting,
"Holy, Holy, Holy . . ." As old Ebenezer slid sideways upon
his pillows, Dr. Reardon bent down; but Lee did not have to be
told that the old man had gone with his Friend. The doctor said,
awed, "Lee, we'll never be any nearer the holy saints than we've
been this day, the two of us!" He glanced up at Lee, sharply.
"You feeling all right, Reverend?"

"Fine," Lee said absently, too full of light to consider his body.
How foolish you had been to worry about Myrtie when the two
worlds were so close together that old Ebenezer could see into
the next room!

For the rest of the day Lee had the strangest feeling, as if he
himself were in two places, too; he could see himself from away
off, having a cup of tea with Myrtie fussing about how exhausted
he looked; while actually he was outside his weary body, alert,
young, and eager, listening for a sound that did not come but for
which he longed with every fiber of his being—the whirr of the
hummingbird's wings. It seemed to his feverish mind that if he
could only hear them again, and understand what they were trying
to tell him, he would know the answers to all the questions which
had been troubling him since he was a little boy lost in the tall
green Texas corn. He shook his head to clear it; you mustn't get
fanciful. But the gold of the sun against the old stone wall had been
so restful, like a benediction; and you were so tired, so very
tired. . . .

"Do you have to go to that Epworth League picnic tonight?" Myrtie worried. "You're too all in, Lee. If you must go, I'll go with you."

"I promised to take them to Willard Park for a cook-out," Lee told her. "They've been counting on it for a month, and you know how kids are. There won't be room for you, sugar, with eight of them, and all the pans and stuff."

But as he drove out of the yard, he looked back at her standing there on the cluttered little back veranda, waving at him; unexpectedly he slammed on Jehu's brakes, got out, went back to take her into his arms. He said with his cheek against her hair, "Remember how the mockingbirds used to sing up in our chinaberry tree in your ma's back yard? The house was wobbly because I didn't have enough nails. 'Turn around, Lee,' you'd order, just as if we were married. 'Don't look. I'm going to climb up now.' We've had a good time, sugar." He strode away from her.

"Lee!" Myrtie gasped. "Wait, I'm going with you!"

But Jehu's engine made such a racket he didn't hear her. She stood there on the sidewalk, staring after him; then she made herself relax. After all, he was going only five miles away on a picnic. . . . She was to wonder frantically later if it would have made any difference if she had gone; for Lee never reached his rendezvous with his young people. Hours later they found him slumped over Jehu's wheel, by the side of the road.

Lee was in the Deaconess Hospital, on whose board of directors he had served so long, for months. The doctors told Myrtie that his sickness was the result of the old automobile accident, when he must have had undetected internal injuries; and she said she'd known all along that Jehu would be the death of him. She caught her breath sharply. Of course Lee would be well in a few more weeks! She was with him every day at the hospital, planning how they'd go down to Newagen as soon as he could be moved, writing hopefully to us children how much better he was. But in her heart, she knew this wasn't true. The faraway look in Lee's eyes frightened her, as did the queer things he kept saying about the hummingbird and the gold. . . . He was delirious; he must be. One night when the hospital didn't send Myrtie away at the closing hour for visitors, she knew the time was getting short. Maybe even tonight. . . . She thrust up her hand to hold her chin steady. Lee mustn't see you cry. When he opened his eyes, Myrtie smiled at him.

"China . . . tree . . ." he said clearly, and then his heavy eye-lids slid down again. Myrtie's heart gave a great leap, for, as usual, she knew what he was thinking. He was trying to tell you that it wasn't all over; he was still going on building a house for you; only this time, instead of a tree hut, it would be the mansion on that star above Newagen. *He was trying to warn you he had to go there first, without you.* With a great effort, she pushed down her panic, listening to the quick, shallow gasp of his breath, forcing herself to remember all those houses they'd lived in, together: big, elegant parsonages and shabby little parsonages, in the city and in the country; but none of them yours. You hadn't even been able to keep Snuggery, the only roof you'd ever loved. But it hadn't mattered, because your real home was wherever Lee was. She bent closer, sobbing aloud. *From now on your home would be wherever Lee had gone. . . .*

We children, Ike, Lillian, V., and Susie, flew back to Boston to be with Myrtie at the funeral. It shouldn't be a funeral at all, Susie told her mother passionately. Remember Dad's "Crown Sermon"? This was his Coronation Day. We'd have only the triumphant parts of the Gospel read—none of that awful "dust to dust" busi-ness—and we'd end with the "Hallelujah Chorus" Dad had loved so well.

"Anything you want," Myrtie agreed woodenly. "That would be nice."

Just before the service, Myrtie was alone at last with Lee in the little room where they'd laid him, dressed in his "good" black pul-pit suit whose shiny lapels she'd brushed so often. "You're supposed to say good-by," she told herself blankly. But how could you say good-by to yourself? He'd been a part of you so long, how could you begin now to walk on one leg? So long as you were alive, Lee would be too. She moved closer, carefully not looking at his un-familiar, fixed-up face; but they couldn't do much to his hands; the freckles on them made them look warm, brown, alive. Lee's dear, freckled hands. She laid her cheek against them and began to hum, softly so the rest wouldn't hear:

"Still, still with Thee, when purple morning breaketh,
When the earth waketh and the shadows flee . . ."

"Isn't she wonderful?" their friends whispered when they saw Myrtie, wearing her last winter's dark-blue hat, sitting there erect between Ike and Susie in the pew. The big auditorium of Tremont Street Church was crowded to the doors with Lee's people who'd loved him during his forty-five years of ministry, some of whom had driven a hundred miles to get here; and sitting regally in the big, carved, pulpit chairs on the platform were the bishop, the president of a great university, dignitaries of the church, come to do Lee honor. But to Myrtie the pulpit was empty; Lee wasn't there. So they said all the nice things and the organist played from the grand, beloved *Messiah;* but the soprano soloist flatted a little, Myrtie thought, and the organ wheezed where it needed fixing. It was better that way, because it was like your life and Lee's together: shabby clothes and shoes from the bargain basement, hamburger instead of steak; but always, up beyond, triumphing over all the little, shabby things, rose the strains of "Hallelujah!" When the organ trumpeted, she got up with the rest, her face lifted, listening.

". . . for the Lord God Omnipotent reigneth,
Hallelujah, Hallelujah. . . ."